Sylvester Stein was born and brought up in South Africa. After a university training in engineering and wartime service in the navy, he switched to journalism, becoming political editor to the *Rand Daily Mail* and later editor of the African magazine *Drum*. In 1957 he came to England and worked as a journalist in Fleet Street until 1963 when he started his own magazine publishing company and founded *Running* Magazine.

In 1972, he took up running at the age of 51. He was one of the founders of the British and International Veterans Running Movement. He has been a British, European and World Champion Veteran runner in the 100m, 200m and 400m and is currently the World Over 60s Silver Medallist in the 100m. He is chairman of the British Veterans Athletic Federation.

Sylvester Stein lives in north London with his second wife Sarah Cawkwell, who is also a runner.

D0250062

The Running Guide
To Keeping Fit

Sylvester Stein

CORGI BOOKS

THE RUNNING GUIDE TO KEEPING FIT

A CORGI BOOK 0 552 12737 X

First publication in Great Britain

PRINTING HISTORY

Corgi edition published 1986

This book is set in 10/11 pt Plantin

Corgi Books are published by Transworld Publishers Ltd.,
61–63 Uxbridge Road, Ealing, London W5 5SA, in Australia
by Transworld Publishers (Aust.) Pty. Ltd., 26 Harley
Crescent, Condell Park, NSW 2200, and in New Zealand by
Transworld Publishers (N.Z.) Ltd., Cnr. Moselle and
Waipareira Avenues, Henderson, Auckland.

Made and printed in Great Britain by the
Guernsey Press Co. Ltd., Guernsey, Channel Islands.

Contents

The Running Guide
To Keeping Fit

1 LET'S DO IT!

Little children of one year old do it, business moguls chasing buses do it, Arab ladies off to Harrods sales do it. Even animated snails do it. Anyone can do it! Anyone can run!

It's easy to run because it's the natural thing to do. People have been running ever since the human race was invented. The human body was constructed to such a curious design especially for the job of walking and running. Thereafter the heart and lungs were built in to provide motive power.

In fact, it's unnatural *not* to run. The heart, lungs and muscles need the work, or they stop functioning properly. However dangerous you might think it is to take up running, it's much more dangerous not to. It's natural and normal to run and everyone has the ability.

I can say this all breezily enough now, but I had to be persuaded of it myself a few years ago. Persuaded! Bullied more like. This friend of mine, Al Rockall, one of the world's lifelong runners, first 'persuaded' me. 'Come on Sylvester,' he commanded, looming there like Lord Kitchener, a menacing forefinger pointing across Regents Park. 'Let's see you jog twice around that first of all.'

I gulped, I winced, I cowered. Why had I ever agreed to have a go?

'Don't worry if it hurts,' he growled, 'I'll be there to keep you moving along nicely.'

I did worry. I could see myself half-way round, completely collapsed, crawling along on all fours, and being lashed onwards by the slave-driving Al.

'Hey, you geezers,' he shouted out when he observed me hanging back – from behind the bushes there jumped these geezers, three team mates of his rigged out in identical shabby track suits.

'Ay, skipper,' they responded and advanced on me with 'persuasive' smiles on their faces. Jogging on the spot, their elbows pumping away in time with each other, they crowded around me. It was clear I had to make an attempt in spite of the fears I had for my heart and other extremely important organs. What a way to treat them, after fifty-one years of useful service, I groaned to myself.

So off we went. There was a certain amount of jogging on my part and a rather greater amount of frog-marching on their part, but you can say that I duly achieved some sort of debut. Oh yes, in the park the little boys laughed and the three hard men produced three evil little chuckles – 'Shall we wheel him into Casualty, Al?' they asked sarcastically at the end – but I had lift-off, I was a runner!

From then on it was easier. For a few weeks it was a case of jog to the first lamp-post, walk to the next, jog and walk and so on – but on my own, thank you very much. I reported in to Al by telephone. Slow, steady improvement followed. I could get round my home block in 8¼ minutes in due course, instead of 11 and then in below the 8. I began to feel strong and confident.

It gets so you become rather too confident. I estimated on the day I did it in 7.53 that not even Steve Ovett could have managed that: after all, one granted, he didn't know the particular course like I did.

Presto, turn the clock on several more years, and taskmaster Al had a world champion in his stable. I'd actually won a gold medal in the Over 60 category of the World Veteran Games, in 1981, at Christchurch, New Zealand.

Not as famous, these games, as the Olympics perhaps, but the competition is as steep and consists of several thousand Over 35 entrants from most countries of the globe. Here's an astonishing thing: These veteran games have not lagged far behind the Olympics in regard to actual times and performances. Less than a generation after someone chalks up an Olympic record a veteran runner has usually eclipsed it.

For instance, Jack Foster of New Zealand in the 1970s, when he was in his mid-forties, raced the marathon in 2:11:19. That was an improvement on any Olympic time prior to 1972 while Joyce Smith, the Englishwoman, a mother of two, marathoned in under

2:29:43 in 1982, aged 43 – this was faster than any *man* had run the distance in the Olympics before 1936.

These are examples of the way the human race is striding ahead and towing along the older runners, who benefit from the effects and experiments of the younger champions, rather as ordinary motor cars do from improvements forged and perfected on Grand Prix racers.

What about this, to show how the improvement at the sharp end, among those in their prime, is in due course taken up by those old enough to be their grandparents? A nice modest man from the United States, Payton Jordan, not long ago set a world record for Over 60 sprinting. He covered 100 metres in 11.8 seconds. Very good running, one would comment cautiously; is it more than that?

It was so good in fact that it rates above the performance of the one-time fastest man in the world, the winner of the 100m in the first of the modern Olympic series, held at Athens in 1896; he was another American, Tom Burke. He took 12 seconds exactly to cover the same distance. I'd like to match those two together on some cinematic time-machine; I wonder who would get the laugh, the man in his 60s, a big white-haired senatorial sort of figure, or the man in his 20s coming in second?

Anyway, Al, my Lord Kitchener coach, and his geezers were very pleased with their protégé and I was pleased too, not only for the medal but because in the years between I'd learned the values of running as a sport, as a way to fitness, as a simple pleasure and as a way to change my life completely. I have now met and known personally many hundreds of men and women who have used running to give them wonderful lives, to help create new confidence in their jobs and marriages – to help them rebuild themselves. That's running as a therapy. It has brought down the heart attack rate and brought up the happiness rate.

We'll be coming to that in words and action but here it's just a reminder to you to get into the running scene, to persevere. Anyone can run, all you need are two legs. Well, *one* would be enough. I raced in New Zealand against a marvellous 60-year-old Australian Keith Crocker, with an artificial leg, who got around 200m in 36 seconds. He stumped away like a jumping jack.

It's not going to happen all in one outing. You need to build up

11

gradually, establishing your training routine week by week, and tucking more jogging miles under your belt. Then the breakthrough; it suddenly gets hold of you – running becomes positive enjoyment, no longer a task.

That's the moment to wait for. At that time, too, surplus weight begins to drop away. As the calories go out you start to feel the runners 'high': when exercising, the body produces an opium-like substance in the brain, the endorphins, which dull pain and make you feel good. That's why many runners claim they're 'hooked'. In my fantasy bodyscan movie, I see these spirited endorphins rushing through my veins and bundling out the round woolly calories.

But more of the battle scenes to come . . . . Here go back to the notion that anyone can succeed in running well, that a typical sedentary character such as myself can emerge from the woodwork in his 50s or 60s and fly along like a youngster.

There you are, that's running: it's natural and normal and it's inside all of us. Every bank manager and window cleaner can do it, every housewife and school teacher. Even animated fleas, even Noel Coward could have done it.

Then again we may not all win world championships, but we can certainly win years of extra life and enjoyment and a victory over flabbiness.

Step forward and do your first run now, the moment the mood takes you. You've just watched the marathon on TV perhaps or heard of the marvellous Dublin women's special, 10,000 Irish girls crowding through the heart of their city, and you feel inspired, at that instant. Go on, 10,000 Irish girls can't be wrong!

Running is simple and it's safe. There's absolutely no need for a preliminary medical check-up *unless* you have some serious history of disease or disablement. How many people have been put off running forever by the thought that they ought to see their GP first? I'm pleased to say that I was responsible for turning my own GP on to running: a distinguished doctor, then President of the College of General Practitioners, he stuck to the pre-dawn hours when nobody could spot His Excellency going along above walking pace.

It's necessary to be blunt about this, to get people out of the rocking chair; out of their mothballed lives in centrally-heated cocoons. Reassure yourself that the most respected of medical experts on running agree that you can safely go ahead on your own.

The comforting truth is that no-one's body has the capacity to go beyond danger level. Go on, try to notch up a 4-minute mile as your maiden effort! It's impossible: the natural governors in the body are automatically brought into play and sit you down to rest after 100 yards or so.

What transpires is that the untrained physique can't summon up a high enough heart rate to go over-fast. Nor has it enough energy to allow it to go over-far. But with regular training the muscles, the heart and the lungs gradually adapt. They actually grow, they become stronger and more experienced. *At any age* you can grow new capillaries in your heart and lung system. Thereafter you can go out and risk yourself on the mile record. People appreciate little enough what capacity they have for running, an activity carried out quite knowledgeably by their mammoth-hunting ancestors.

No one had less knowledge of how good she might be as a runner than Jenny Wood Allen of Dundee. Nor did she dream of fame. Here she was, a local councillor and busy committee person, who simply decided one day she would 'show them'. She was going to enter the Dundee marathon, and was spurred on by the negative attitude of others.

She chose December to start in training . . . . nice time of the year in Dundee, cold, wet, windy; with luck some early snow. Not four months later she went right round the 26.2 miles of the marathon course in 5 hours 34 minutes. The weather was still cold, wet and windy, with, lucky lady, a good bit of snow.

Then more remarkable, in 1985, two years and five marathons later she ran Dundee again, in a world record for a woman Over 70 – 4:21.

Yes she could do it. *Anyone* could do it.

2 THE REWARDS OF RUNNING

Here's a ready-made set of lyrics; when put to music you get a hummable little song. It's the list of things that running will do for you:

> Running will tone up the body, toughen the heart; it will lift the spirit, hot up the sex drive: keep down the weight when you give up on smoking; it's a sport for all the family, a joy in itself; it matures the young and recharges the old. It puts a smile on the face of humanity and bells on its toes.

One day I hope to prove that running can also pay off the mortgage, solve parking problems and bring heaven a little closer. Meanwhile we shouldn't forget its simple, old-fashioned advantage in getting you from A to B a bit faster.

What's bad about it? Criticisms aimed at the running boom over the years do not add up to a long list, although they're sometimes rather vindictive. The major item, repeated over and over, is that running causes 'injury'; I plan to clear up misconceptions about that in a later chapter.

How is running able to provide this great and wonderful variety of benefits? From the fitness that running brings into existence. Each benefit derives from the starting point that running gives you a strong and healthy heart and a healthy heart helps you to live longer while living more fully. That, after all, *is* fitness. It is the primary benefit; it is not only a benefit in itself, but it's the base for the other major benefits. Once you're fit, the glow of fitness radiates in all directions.

Here's a typical case history to show the workings of this chain of causes and effects. The sedentary person, with flabby figure and under-exercised heart, goes in for jogging. That, through the aerobic effect, strengthens the heart, lessening the chances of heart disease and giving the essential physical fitness. This physical fitness, this toning up of the body, is what makes the listless person actually 'feel good'; it does wonders for stamina, sex drive, ability to work and to combat stress, and general enjoyment. Furthermore, the physical fitness in turn boosts the psychological fitness, which helps with such problems as weight and smoking.

That is why we put fitness at the top of the benefits of running.

Fitness

When you start to run regularly your body begins a slow but permanent change, what we laymen think of as a change in its metabolism. Your joints, muscles and ligaments actually change, they become more flexible. The heart, itself a muscle, changes too. The heart, with the lungs, becomes more efficient in its working.

You become a trimmer shape all round as the other muscles firm up – it is, after all, the muscles that help to hold the body in shape.

Everything about you changes – in general you're trading in your old body for an improved version, a fitter version.

Test Your New Fitness

You're sure to *feel* fitter once you're a regular runner. But you can actually prove that you *are* fitter, that there are changes to your body capable of being measured. You can do this by making simple before-and-after measurements on yourself. Here's a do-it-yourself kit for the purpose, much cheaper than expensive tests and check-ups. Test yourself when you start running, again after six weeks, then after six months.

You'll need:

1. Camera, for producing Before and After photographs.
2. Bathroom scales, for weight comparisons.
3. Stop Watch, to count pulse beats.
4. Tape-measure, to go round girth.
5. Staircase or bench, for doing Step-Up test.

1. *Start with the camera*: Get someone to snap you in a standing position, face on. Stick the photo up on the bathroom mirror. Get a snap after each of the two later stages, dressed the same way and in the same position. Stick them alongside, then note the changes. I hope they'll be something like this: *Week One*: Sloppy doughy figure, uncertain look on the face, *Week Six*: Not much change to perceive, except perhaps a smug look on the face. *Month Six*: Shape redistributed, to give a lean trim figure, with firmer lines and a more determined expression on the face. A better-looking human being. I have a whole gallery of before and after pictures of friends who've taken up running.

2. *Weigh yourself*: This should help you to put actual numbers to the evidence shown in the photographs. It will be useful to have a record of the new weight, to make certain it comes down and stays down.

3. *Take your pulse*: Count the number of beats per minute at your wrist or your throat, or simply the number of thuds when your hand is on your chest. Do this in bed upon waking. Within weeks the pulse rate will come right down; it's quite a sensational effect, and will give you confidence that you're on the way. This is a measurement that a doctor will regard as having significance. A beginner's pulse will drop from the sedentary person's average of 72 beats a minute, (even higher in the very unfit) right down to the 50s and 60s and even, with some wiry marathon runners, to 35 or 40. It is a well-known joke in running circles that one's examination at the doctor's often gives him alarm. 'Mr Cullinan,' my friend's GP once said to him nervously, 'I'll have to take your pulse all over again; and your blood pressure, I'm afraid.' There seemed to be some doubt in his mind as to whether Cullinan was still alive. At the least he disbelieved the evidence of his instruments, which showed a pulse of 38 and the blood pressure of a man in his 20s, though his patient was 58. This was a standard occurrence until quite recently when medical men began to take up running themselves.

The figures rarely lie: a low pulse is an accepted indicator of vitality and vigour, so there you have a straight read-out of the fact that one's metabolism has undergone a favourable change.

4. *Measure Up*: Write your waistline readings on the photographs. Expect a definite decrease.

5. *Step-Up*: This test gives a reading of one's ability to handle continued effort and the body's capacity to return to normal rapidly. An improved recovery time is good news for the heart.

The Harvard step-up test requires you to step from the floor on to a sturdy bench 20in high, and down again, 30 times a minute for four minutes. You must straighten the knee fully each time. (If you get too tired to go on, you can stop earlier but this will lower your score).

As soon as you finish, sit quietly and take your pulse, for 30 seconds one minute after you finish, another 30 seconds two minutes after you finish, and another 30 seconds three minutes after you finish.

You compute your Recovery Index (RI) by using this formula:

$$RI = \frac{\text{Duration of exercise in secs} \times 100}{\text{Sum of pulse counts} \times 2}$$

If your RI is 60 or less, your rating is poor; between 61 and 70 fair; between 71 and 80 good; between 81 and 90 very good; any more is amazing. But the best way to use the test is in comparing your RI when you start running with what it is when you have become a regular runner – it should move well upwards.

The important point about these tests is that they show that the benefits of running can be written down in figures. Contrast this with claims for fads and fancy diets, which rely on sentiment, charisma and anecdotes for back-up evidence. Even many a public committee on better health and fitness comes out with nothing but hopeful exhortations to the population. They advise this or that change in food habits, but have to add coyly that they cannot actually prove statistically it will reduce heart attack, or otherwise promote health. Whereas it can be *proved* that on the one hand smoking is bad for you, and on the other running is good for you. There have been great volumes of evidence on smoking since the post-war work by Richard Doll and on running since the early

17

publications on jogging by Kenneth Cooper, the man who brought aerobics into fashion.

Running and Smoking

Running helps to kill the cigarette habit. Once you're fit it's much easier to give up smoking. A two-pack-a-day man, or a two-fags-a-day girl . . . . neither of them can hold out against this remarkable cure. It's one of the most amazing and least documented of phenomena, how running does the trick. It just seems to happen naturally. You may not give up immediately, but soon enough you cut down, then give up completely.

'Well, of course!' cries the opposition, 'you do respond and for the very reason that you are already biased against smoking . . . . have you not taken up running specifically to assist you to give up?'

It's not too difficult to dispose of this counter-attack; how few people succeed who go in for other cigarette cures! In 1985, of those who went on a course and even paid for the privilege to break themselves of the habit, only about 15 per cent were successful. Even with the nicotine-flavoured chewing gum cure prescribed by doctors, as many as 80 per cent are still smoking after a year.

All these people are driven by a desperate desire to avoid the death sentences pronounced by medical science on smokers: lung cancer, stomach cancer, heart failure, pneumonia. They're specifically trying to do something about it. Yet they can't.

With new runners the story is remarkably different: After six months only 7 per cent are still smoking. More government money needs to be spent on publicising this major health advantage.

How does this sensational cure work? What makes it stick? Firstly, you'll find that smoking is directly counter-productive to training, by interfering with your breathing. That and the discomfort of a tight chest and a cough will add to the incentive to give up.

Secondly, as a fit athlete you'll find that in some manner you've become sensitised against cigarettes and your body will automatically reject the habit.

Smoking thrives on intense, non-physical situations, like leaning on bar-counters, sitting exams and all-night poker sessions, when the heart and lungs are working half-steam.

When you are very active, however, with your lungs expanded and oxygen and blood pumping through your bloodstream, you will not welcome the noxious intrusion of cigarette smoke.

Thirdly, when you become fit, you experience 'runner's high', a pleasant sensation which can replace the need for the high nicotine. When you exercise your brain produces those endorphins, which mimic the effect of morphine, a good substitute for the drug craved by smokers.

A smoker's tale

No case better illustrates the advantages to a smoker of taking up running than that of Peter McGhie, a language consultant of Swiss Cottage, London, now in his early 40s. Did Peter have some premonition that he was marked out for lung cancer, one wonders.

Peter's story can give hope to people who despair about the years of smoking behind them and say that it's too late to give up.

Peter proved that you can act before lung cancer and death strike you down. But he was only just in time. When he was 39 he decided to take up running, mainly as a stratagem for giving up cigarettes.

'Maybe the idea of running was a signal telling me that the cancer was there and I should do something about it,' he said to me. 'It became the classic tale of wheezing wreck to Marathon Man. I used to be a heavy smoker and I had quite a bit of weight to shed as well. Slowly but surely I progressed and the breathing cleared, the pounds dropped off and my body found undreamed-of functioning levels.'

He joined a club and by the end of a year he could run a very useful 10 miles in 60 minutes. Turning 40 gave him the extra incentive of winning medals in veteran competition. This pushed him below the 56 minutes 30 mark for 10 miles (nearly 11 miles an hour). Then he completed the London Marathon in 2:39 and set himself the magic target of 2½ hours. So he entered the Poly Marathon, which goes through the grounds of Windsor Castle, hoping to break this next barrier.

But something went wrong with his running. It was only because he *was* a runner, trained to 'listen to his body', that he could sense that in fact there was something wrong with his body. And that led him to the early diagnosis that saved him.

The plan in doing the Poly Marathon was to shepherd his slower clubmate Blaine Tomlinson through it. Blaine was to hang on to him as long as possible, before Peter would speed up and leave Blaine to follow.

After a mile of running, however, it was Blaine who was itching to speed ahead, looking over his shoulder and asking 'Are we going fast enough, Pete,' and it was Peter who was struggling. At 10 miles, Blaine took off fast, leaving Peter floundering, and ran an excellent 2:48. Peter was almost an hour behind and then he knew something was wrong. So the next day he called into the local GP and told him how he'd felt low and dreadfully weak, and tight in the chest. 'Nothing at all,' the doctor reassured him on examination, and told his wife behind Peter's back that it was probably 'all in the mind'. But Peter wasn't satisfied and went back to see another man in the same practice – again the diagnosis was 'quite normal'. However, he was ahead of the doctors. Shortly afterwards he needed to go to Bath on a special university course and arrived there *flattened*. He consulted the campus doctor and insisted on admission to the local hospital for tests. Sure enough, X-rays showed up an ominous shadow on the left lung which a biopsy confirmed as a cancerous tumour of the virulent oat-cell variety.

'Despite the previous warnings, my immediate reaction was still a kind of stunned "I demand a recount!" incredulity.'

Apparently the cancer *was* already there, a small growing speck of it, before he had left off smoking – officially you need to give up for as long as five years before being absolutely sure you are safe and clear.

'Then my mind fastened onto the practicalities of what, if anything, could be done. Surgery was impossible because the tumour site was close to the central 'plumbing'. However, the doctor mentioned a new and very tough form of drug treatment that had been developed, the problem being that it carried such drastic side-effects that only the fit and strong could hope to survive it. I volunteered like a shot, and clinched the matter by citing my odd pastime of running marathons. He agreed that if I could endure those then I could endure just about anything.

'And so it turned out. From Bath I was referred to the cancer unit at University College Hospital and was soon undergoing the dreadful treatment. I will draw a veil over the next few weeks, which I would not go through again for a chestful of BT shares. Suffice to say that I emerged looking like Kojak after a stay in a concentration camp. Those who saw John Hurt in the film *Champions* will get the general idea. But it had worked. X-rays and other tests revealed that there was now no trace of the tumour. I still had to undergo an intensive course of radiotherapy as a precautionary measure, and there was always the chance (there still is) that the disease might return, but basically I was completely free of it, at least for the foreseeable future.

'Now, all this had understandably left me feeling extremely washed out and drained, and my thoughts turned again to running as a means of trying to get back some kind of physical form. All I could manage at first were a few shuffling steps round the block, strangely reminiscent of when I originally took up running, but I can hardly describe the elated sense of achievement to be out and alive and moving. Painfully slowly my strength began to build up week by week, and I decided to set my sights on an event – the Burnham Beeches half-marathon.' (He finished in 1:53 and later that Autumn brought his time down to 1:43.) 'It was the body-awareness of running that led to my crucially early diagnosis, it was the fundamental strength of running that sustained me through the drastic treatment, and it is running that has inspired and aided my recovery.'

More Benefits

Stress

Running deals swiftly with stress, perhaps through burning off the excess nervous energy bottled up inside you. Yet it can't be due to that alone, for the stress starts to fall away when you're a few steps into your run, well before the energy has been fully broached. Probably a run gives you a chance to break out of the cycle of stress, which is self-perpetuating.

The advice you are given when you're in a stressful situation is 'Relax'. This is no help at all because you're much too worked up to try. But go out through the door in your running kit and you're lulled into a new rhythm – the stress obediently and immediately sheds itself.

Whatever the reason, there's nothing so efficacious for the tired business executive or the strained over-achiever.

Sex

No one other than myself has yet done a survey on the new wave of sex that has swept through the ranks of veteran runners. All, when asked the question 'Has running improved your sex life?', simply gave me a knowing wink and left it at that. I took this to be a very positive sign. The main reason is not hard to spot: sex is an active physical matter, for sure, and runners are physically in very good shape. Keep going!

Social

You find a thousand new friends on the running trail – the problem is to keep up with them all. My way is to throw a Sunday afternoon barbecue plus a jog-in party every so often!

Weight problems

One of the greatest benefits of fitness is in improving your shape without the need for dieting. In fact that's of such major value that we ought to give it a chapter to itself . . . .

3   EAT, DRINK AND BE SLIMMER

Worry no more about diet when you take up running; eat what you like, drink what you fancy (a *little* of what you fancy!) and be as merry a soul as any King Cole. Dropping a stone or more of weight is much better done by running than by any other method, and it is permanent . . . . thanks to the changes in metabolism that running creates.

It very much parallels the smoking story, in that traditional slimming cures, too, rarely have a lasting effect. Dieting, starving, eccentric systems of nutrition, appetite-limiting drugs, machines that aim to roll your flesh away, Fatties Anonymous of various kinds, hypnotism, Turkish baths and other weird treatments all call for unbelievable supplies of willpower, which few people are able to keep on handing out. If successful they might bring their weight down fast, but in one big eating binge it all goes back on again. Dieting is a life sentence of self-denial.

A great percentage of would-be slimmers never get cured at all. Year after year they despairingly go back to rejoin the very same classes with the hope again of becoming half presentable for the bikini season. It is all most unscientific and commercial too; someone once counted over 4,000 different diets in the slimming literature, all unproven, none put to scientific test and most of them in conflict with one another – eat fat, don't eat fat and so on. Some of them become best-sellers for a while, then fade away, leaving a number of chubby bodies stranded above high-water mark.

Which? magazine once did a thorough set of tests on fashionable diets and slimming products. After their guinea pigs had tried almost everything on the market and been checked and measured, the verdict was 'Don't waste your money'. The only items found to be at all helpful were low-calorie drink and food substitutes, and then only when used as part of a calorie-controlled diet. Some *very* low calorie, high-protein diets they said, should positively be avoided, while appetite suppressants, if they worked at all, didn't do so for long.

But running! Running works slowly, steadily and without fuss and, because it is a radical cure, changing the shape and composition of the body, has a lasting effect. The runner does not have to worry about willpower, the inches slowly roll off of their own free will.

How gratifying it is, once you are regularly into running, to eat what you like, without adding layers of what the slimming trade calls 'unsightly fat' to your outline. If you do go on a binge now and then, you can simply run it off in no time.

The Reasons Why

There are several reasons why runners stay slender, and why even the big man or woman keeps a trim shape.

The first reason is the obvious one, that running burns up the calories. How does that come about? Consider the whole body process. In the first place we eat to provide energy for living. The food we animals devour in eating is for the most part converted inside us into usable fuel. In the body this fuel burns away quietly to keep us warm-blooded and to produce the energy, counted in calories, that we use when moving around, working, dancing, loving, fighting. If we aren't very active, but *are* very greedy, the calories aren't demanded as fuel and linger on in the body, stored in the flesh and showing up as flabby deposits. The marathoner, however, even if a hearty eater, jogs away a good bit, literally burning up some of these stores on the run.

The second reason for runners staying slim and lean-looking concerns the very method adopted by their bodies to pack away the spare calories that have been stuffed into them. The food *they* eat, when digested, turns into muscle and sinew and migrates to the muscly parts of the body instead of adding yet more layers of fat to the flabby parts such as waistline or upper thighs, the well known spare tyres and jug-handles, as in the case of sedentary people.

So the runners become firmer and appear more shapely.

This happens to any person taking exercise because the body

24

knows it is required to perform hard work, and decides, very wisely, to convert any new food supply into muscle. It is no good objecting by saying 'How could the body make an intelligent decision like that?' It does, that is quite simply what the training effect does for you when you give the body work to do. It assumes there will be another demand coming up and prepares for it. Thus, each time you use your muscles their own appetite and need for fuel supplies is sharpened. (And who cares if *they* put on weight!)

To see this in real life, compare the experiences of the two characters, Road Runner and Armchair Fatty, when tucking into a large slice of cheese cake. Fatty finds that after digesting it, it gets deposited in the form of yet more body fat. The runner eats the same cake, but the digestive processes in this case turn it straight into muscle, adding further outlines to existing muscles, which are located in far more photogenic places than the waist or the sloppy backs of the upper arms.

It is just as hard luck on Fatty when he or she tries strict dieting or fasting. The very opposite then occurs; muscle is lost equally with the fat. It is obviously a real drawback to lose muscle or other lean body tissue, whereas, as was demonstrated in a famous medical experiment, athletes on a slimming course find that they lose nothing *but* their body fat. They keep all their muscle and tendon – because the body knows it will be demanded.

So, at the end of the day, Fatty looks round and wobbly, whether on a diet or not, and Runner looks good. It's just a question of how and where the intake is distributed and packed away.

It is possible that in the early stages of a running career one might earn a better shape and yet not actually lose weight. Here is the case history of a new girl runner who was disappointed because she was faced with just this problem: 'I weigh 9st 7lb; I have a small frame and am only 5ft 4in tall and feel that I have too much fat especially around the buttocks and thighs. A month ago, I began running six times a week for at least 35 minutes per session. I also began a diet and, showing uncharacteristic self-discipline, I have stuck to both. I would have thought that, after a month, the bathroom scales would reflect an encouraging loss of at least a few pounds. But not a thing!

I have noticed a difference in muscle tone and shape in my legs, but why haven't I lost any weight?'

She presented her problem for the attention of Dr Craig Sharp, the physiologist, who sent her this reply:

'It is common for people to take up an exercise schedule and fail to lose weight in the early weeks. Although you may not yet be losing much weight, your body composition almost certainly will be changing in quite a pronounced way. The amount of fat in your body will have decreased, while that of other constituents, like muscle, tendon, bone and blood, will have increased. Often, for the first few weeks, the gains and the losses balance out, so you remain the same weight. Some people may even *gain* a few pounds! However, by the 10-12 week period, your weight should have started to show an obvious decrease. Your muscles respond to exercise by making marked internal changes which enable you to get more energy from them – so you run faster and further. You have already noticed changes in your muscles – they have become firmer and your shape is changing. At the same time your tendons will be getting thicker and stronger, and so will your bones at the points where the tendons from the muscles make their attachments.

'Your heart, which is simply another muscle, will also be getting slightly heavier as it responds to the training, and your blood volume will increase by at least a pint.'

That's exactly the point. What slimmers want to achieve is a better shape, not to be so round and dimply – and to get rid of the cellulite! It's not solely a case of pounds avoirdupois – no one really needs to lose weight as such, though that's how it's usually reckoned up.

Why should anyone except a racing jockey want to lose *weight*? H.G. Wells, in one of his early stories, made this paradox his theme. He wrote about a fat man who got in the clutches of a wise but wicked witch whom he asked to give him some magic that would lose him weight. Alas, she double-crossed him by doing exactly what he asked. He ended up weightless – lighter than air, and having to wear lead weights in his boots to save himself from being blown away. But he was as round and fat as ever.

The third reason, to take up the list again, why running turns out to be the best way to a better figure is the improved motivation it provides for the runner. It stiffens up the runner's resolve in a number of ways. There is the basic desire to get slimmer, but there is also the wish to improve one's running performance, which is made easier with a leaner figure. So you're fighting with a double-edged weapon. The weight-conscious runner is measuring himself or herself not only against the bathroom scales, but against improved times in getting round the park, and is jealous of any unnecessary flab, which would hinder the process. It's a question as much of taking off two seconds as taking off two pounds. There is a double incentive.

The runner is also motivated by the same drug effect in the brain that works to beat smoking. That drug reproduces the 'runner's high'; the generous amounts of oxygen streaming around the system boost the runner's willpower. What wouldn't the slimmer give for an extra few ounces of natural willpower when trying to say no to another helping of Coq au Vin.

So far the runner has gained, therefore, by having more incentive to bring down the weight, and more willpower to apply behind that incentive. There is yet another minor effect that helps: when you are planning to go out on a run, or even more notably, to join a race, you simply feel the need to avoid stuffing yourself, if only because of the discomfort to be expected from burdening the stomach with undigested food, whether crisps and cream puffs or good innocent salad. It pays to take nothing at all on board for three or four hours before a run, which automatically cuts out one more temptation.

Until now the message has been to use running as a base if aiming to kill off either the smoking habit or the over-eating habit, but there is an important sense in which the two themes are linked, in which the one acts, unhappily, to counter the other. Many a large lady has made this connection, arguing that she dare not drop smoking, even to save her life, because her weight would straight-away shoot upwards. Could it be *possible*, one mutters, to add further to those porky outlines? Would not her dear friends rather have her continue porky than pass out of this life altogether? And was it not the compulsive eater in her that enlarged her in the first place?

Yet while we snigger we must admit that there could be some truth in her plaint, because anyone will appreciate food more when blessed with an appetite improved through the heightened sense of taste and smell that comes from giving up cigarettes. Most definitely, enjoyment of food is deliciously increased!

What a calamity, whimpers Fatty, as if I didn't enjoy it enough already.

Be assured, madam, running will deal with both problems in one. Once into running, you may eat and enjoy the best of foods, their true tastes revealed again after years to a palate that had become dulled by smoking. Eat and grow slim, if ever it could be proclaimed!

Softly, Softly

It is, however, important to get the timing right, to take on these three items in the correct order: starting to run, losing weight and giving up smoking. Don't shoulder them all at the same time; they each demand some degree of willpower – and who in the world could be expected to muster triple-strength willpower? Start with running, remembering that once into it, the other two will follow naturally, without the need to deploy further willpower. Easy does it.

In this matter I summon for the defence one of the most famous and successful guinea pigs in this willpower business, Geoffrey Cannon, best-selling author and fun runner. Geoffrey, then editor of Radio Times, a corpulent, chain-smoking, overstressed executive if ever there was one, began his battle for fitness as he approached the age of 40. He took on the wayward fat man inside himself and won.

He began jogging! On his birthday he joined the Veterans, my own particular club, and we sometimes ran together. I saw the fascination running and fitness had for him; over the years it became more and more his life, until he turned full-time to working up his books on the subjects and abandoned the editor's desk. He brought a penetrating mind to bear on the struggle for fitness and attacked it with enterprise, making a note of all he learned from his own and others' experiences. Most of these others were people he press-ganged – hundreds of them – into one of his many experimental groups. He was a leader among guinea pigs! Here is his advice on the crucial issue of timing for those about to

28

start exercise: 'I know you are thinking of stopping drinking, stopping smoking, changing your eating habits as well as starting to exercise. Please don't. Just start to exercise. Give yourself permission to smoke, drink, eat terrible food. Then, after maybe three months, see how you feel. You may feel like stopping smoking, for example. But don't *try*.'

He discovered that as a result of this technique, tested out by him on dozens of those in his groups, about half of the people who had been smokers at first, stopped. They stopped quite automatically, without the need for willpower; they said it was no effort. 'Others, like me, for whom it was still an effort, were helped by the boost in self-confidence and self-image given them,' Geoffrey adds.

'Very important: take it one step at a time. One other advantage is that the increased metabolic rate as a result of exercise makes it much less likely that weight will be gained if the exerciser stops smoking.'

Not only Geoffrey Cannon but a great many of his one-time guinea pigs found that as well as their shapes their lives were changed by running.

Compare them with the misguided regiments of men and women – mostly women – who have been pawns in the slimming game these past fifty years. Think how many millions have martyred themselves for the sake of diets that have since been discredited. It's not bad enough that the high-protein diet can cause kidney problems, that the high-fat diet can cause depression, that the high-carbohydrate diet can increase diabetic risk, that appetite suppressants can bring about blurred vision and palpitations, that diuretics can leave the victim dizzy and with leg cramps, that laxative diets can cause diarrhoea, that bulk-producing agents may cause gastro-intestinal disturbances, that starch blockers don't work and that thyroid hormone is potentially dangerous in those with a heart condition. No, the worst is that the diets are mostly ineffective in making you slimmer, even if you are able to bear with them. Was there ever such a hoax played on men and women?

The truth is that slimming diets are bunk. It is simple to see why they have so small a chance of working if you realise that they do nothing to change your metabolism. Could eating forkfulls of fibre change your fat into lean muscle? Could starving conscientiously on grapefruit breakfasts do so? Could low-carbohydrate or high-carbohydrate? Or less sugar and more saccharine? They might make you temporarily less bulgy, but they won't keep you that way, unless you stick permanently and rigorously to the diet. In the end the only diet that has any real hope of working is one in which you simply eat less, and even that does not change the compositon of your body and the distribution of your fat muscle: even that makes no permanent difference to your metabolism, as running or other exercise does.

Liberty Hall

It's my view that the same overall principle applies to most nutritional advice now being spread downwards from government and medical institutions through the retail food trade to house-wives. At best the new eating habits they are encouraging might be of value so long as you follow them, but they have no permanent effect on your body's condition.

Is it possible for a layman such as myself, a mere runner, to criticise these eminent authorities? It is, because they themselves acknowledge when announcing their strictures on eat-no-fat, eat-less-salt and so on that they have no actual *proof* that they are right, although they believe it in their hearts. I would prefer to see hard statistical proof before accepting their scare stories; I wish they would take their hands off their hearts. Is it not possible for them to set up ten thousand or so guinea pigs and ten thousand controls and check whether anyone comes to harm through an old fashioned roast beef and vegetables diet, or through which ever other foods are being incriminated? Just as we know quite positively today, through counting up and comparing, that smokers die young, why is it not possible to count up the relative illnesses and mortalities of the roast beef and the wholemeal bread eaters? If there is a significant difference to be noted, let us all hear of it. So far there is just inference, anecdote and opinion.

So my advice is, eat what food you like until there is harder evidence. Certainly, once you are a runner and quit of the fear of what eating will do to your weight and shape, you may take a much more relaxed view generally of food fads and fashions. Most of these are whims, based on censorious and ungenerous philosophies promoted by schools of alternative health-conselling which seem to construct diets out of nothing but the less edible forms of vegetable life – to strengthen moral fibre, no doubt. They are not checked out in scientific tests.

Be guided by taste, nature's own diet guide. It has been tested by experience and developed over millions of years; the human taste equipment is there not just to tell you what is nice and what is nasty, but what is good for you and what is bad, and what is positively poisonous. Things taste pleasant or not, in fact, precisely because they are good for you or not. The body knows what it needs.

It is through his highly complicated and sensitive taste mechanism that man has survived all these years and developed so successfully. The principle of taste has kept him pointed accurately in the direction of tasty (good) foodstuffs and away from tasteless and unpalatable (bad) items and it has also directed him to imbibe the right *proportions* of each health-giving food; carbohydrate, protein, liquid, vitamins and necessary trace elements. That is the way our remarkable species has evolved.

How does this balancing machinery work? Again through taste, sensed at the tip of the tongue, much as with a snake, and backed up by the palate and by evidence provided by the nose. Taste tells us eventually, after wolfing down a large and delicious plateful of joint and potatoes, that we do not want to go on eating more of this after all, thank you. A message goes from the satisfied digestive system up to the brain, and then from the brain over to the tongue with instructions to stop further deliveries of protein and carbohydrate. Enough! This the tongue converts into taste sensations, which send instructions back again to the brain telling it that the body is bored with the main dish. The human being who thinks he is directing all these actions feels he is 'full up'. But he's not of course, only full of the basic constituents of his diet – there is still room for pudding let's say, and a delicate savoury dish – because the body still demands tiny supplies of certain special additives to be found in a bowl of fruit or a Welsh Rarebit or a glass of Chartreuse.

Drink is also vital for the body, yet we take it in only for the reason that we think we are 'thirsty' and enjoy the taste of tea or orange juice, but 'thirsty' is simply the taste buds' interpretation of urgent orders emerging from the liquid channels and realms of our insides.

So for millions of years of evolution mankind has been eating the correct diet and drinking the correct liquids, depending on supplies available, with adjustment instructions programmed into the body's nervous system. Memory, habit and social custom have reinforced the tasting equipment and made us competent to handle the information quite casually without the need at every mouthful or before every meal to work it all out again as so many calories or so many international vitamin units. Only in the past few decades have we become self-conscious and calculating in our diet due to confused and conflicting advice from unlicensed therapists and oversolicitous scientists. Stop worrying and enjoy your food!

We are what we are and we have got that way through what we have eaten. The human species evolved as the perfect exploiter of food supplies in its environment. That is as much as to say that the species was tailor-made to fit around the diet. Conversely we have to keep our diet tailored to the species. The diet of the past is therefore still the right diet for today. And taste, which was the only guide to that diet of the past, is still the best diet guide today.

To rely on natural taste is to put the individual safely on the road to ideal health. Taste will expect and demand three decent meals a day. It will soon enough object if there is too much or too little of what it needs; it will soon enough rebel if its meals are repetitive and uninteresting, because it demands novelty, a rotation of different foods to provide different specialised trace ingredients.

The variety and amount of foods in the menu of an ordinary properly-run household will contain everything needed by the normal body. Such an ordinary diet will ensure that the individual with his own personal taste sensors is protected from taking in too much of this element or too little of that.

It must be understood that we are not addressing children here; they are wayward eaters, with uneducated codes and they will or will not eat what's good for them – they will devour a day's work of banana-flavoured crisps perhaps – they must be watched over.

32

We are no longer talking about slimming problems, we are talking here of food as it relates to fitness and health, so-called health foods. It is clear that anyone who eats and eats, beyond the call of taste, will put on weight. That is one of the disadvantages of modern civilisation; it commands such plenty that people may indulge themselves all day and every day on food brought in from the corners of the universe, stored away too conveniently to hand; nor are the self-indulging required to work off their meals in the exercise of hunting or harvesting, which was a useful controlling device to protect against consistent overeating.

Now it is only too easy to go on the binge and stay on the binge.

The tongue will tell the runner all he or she needs to know beyond that need for limitation of quantity. The tongue will guide the sensible person safely past the stacks of convenience foods, for after all they don't boast the excellence of flavour to be found in fresh, homecooked meals.

So it is Liberty Hall for the regular mature runner. Sit down to the flavoursome traditional dishes that have become notorious of late. Comfort yourself, you regular runners, with the thought that at the very worst, you'll burn it all off on your next outing.

Fear not these censured foods. Nor equally, be driven towards supposedly 'good' foods. Who has been able to measure, with any degree of certainty the value to health of a strictly measured-out diet of whole foods, health foods and 'natural' foods? Has it been proved that they are sounder than even the worst junk foods?

A fortiori, it is no use hoping that specialised extracts of this or that are going to improve your performance as a runner. They are illusions; my advice is to eat what tastes good to you, and ignore the diet plans and commercial recipes offered to distance runners; they are magic, not science, they are myth and mystery never yet put to the genuine test. Chocolate, vitamin C, glucose, carbohydrate overloading – where's the evidence? The once highly-regarded carbo-loading system, even, lives on purely in the ceremony of the pasta party. Who knows if that has ever brought down by a single second anyone's marathon time!

No, you cannot eat your way to a world record or a personal best. That can come only from training.

4 SIX EASY WEEKS

If you're about to set out on your first run, take care – know that you're committing yourself to a lifetime's enjoyment. Yes, once you have your first tentative weeks behind you, you'll realise running has become addictive, and a way of life, not just some passing craze.

Running is not merely a beneficial course of treatment, it provides pure, positive pleasure, hence its addictive powers. You take it up because it's good for you, then it won't let go. It really ought to carry a government warning! When readers of *Running* Magazine were asked how long they intended to keep up interest in their pursuit, 97 per cent of them said 'For the rest of my life'.

But to get yourself, as a beginner, through those first weeks is the hardest thing, to successfully arrive at the situation where you are 'hooked' and have truly become a runner. That's the aim of this chapter, to help turn you on.

Most people fall at the very first hurdle, they never get out at all despite their good resolutions, and that will be the problem we start with, the crucial one. How to get you up and running? The main enemy here is your own inertia, which advises you that it costs much less energy to stay at home warmly dressed up, stretched out in the easy chair. 'Budge not,' says the fiend! 'Turn on *Dallas*,' says the fiend!

If you do get your debut done, the second outing could be almost as sizeable an obstacle. The poor runner on that first day has perhaps felt like some abject slug beside the old hands and may have slunk home swearing never to emerge again . . . . disgrace . . . . early retirement!

Even after a week or two people drop out because they see no benefits yet from such an amount of brutal struggle. Instant results are what they want. A woman I know, a one-time beauty queen of Southend, now rather rotund, wrote off the whole business for good when she rushed onto the scales after four or five days of tentative jogging and found she hadn't yet knocked off half a stone. Back to her diet . . . . on which she gradually grew plumper over the years.

So that's the task, to get new runners into the network and keep them there and it's clear that we need a specially constructed system to bring us through those difficult few weeks, a nice easy, comfortable introductory course.

All that's wanted on your part is a little patience, with the realisation that the blessings of running grind slow but they grind exceeding sure. And they last.

To demonstrate that one does duly arrive at the desired blissful state, to act as an encouragement, I here log up a typical beginner's experience for you.

Day One Out of breath after three minutes; feel sweaty after five. Quite sure everyone is commenting on my puffy flesh . . . . legs and arms pink and mottled. Shoes go slap-slap on the path, very embarrassing.

Week One Pretty breathless still and still feeling foolish. Stiffness in left calf, rather worrying. Some kids shouting remarks in first lap, couldn't face them a second time. Shoes pinch anyway. So where *are* these benefits?

Week Two Keeping at it, a certain *sang froid* now. Feel quite chirpy after a shower. Chirpier after a beer.

Week Six Jogging comfortably for short distances, chatting the while maybe and pleased with myself – chuffed rather than puffed. Boasting real road shoes and a T-shirt that announces it was first prize at the Bahamas Prison Indoor Marathon. After the run: a glow of well-being.

Week Ten I've tapered down my smoking without even trying, (running is replacing one addiction with another). A couple of pounds have got whittled away, from the right places, too (no sign of 'cellulite' going as yet). I now discover a new fast gear and am gaining confidence at work too.

Month Four Harder running effort is now producing quite substantial changes. Smoking has gone right overboard. Stomach and thighs receding. Nearly every race is a personal record; at work I don't feel so jaded.

Year One A minor hold-up due to a sore knee needed a week's rest and exercises. Back in again, better than ever, with that feeling of lifelong fitness, lifelong youth. I'm learning to get more out of myself and am picking up new techniques.

Years Two and Three Becoming leaner and trimmer, no signs of reaching one's 'plateau' yet.

That's to convince you that running's worth a fair trial. You've got to give it that fair trial, to get beyond Week Six at the least – the magic in running takes some time to work. It isn't like some faddy hit-and-run diet or a pack of tranquillisers. You don't come down two stone in a fortnight, only to see it surreptitiously pile on again. Nor do you ever need a knock-out drop to get a night's sleep.

No, when you become a runner, slow but definite rearrangements occur in your body. Fat slowly moves off the hips, muscle slowly accumulates in the legs. Also sleep patterns become normal, perhaps because the mind becomes more contented once the body has.

I've seen all this a hundred times, and conversely I have never observed a single regular runner who has put on weight. Each crop of recruits steadily takes on a new, taut look. It's a frequent thing with me to find myself saying in surprise to some acquaintance or another: 'Jim, you're quite lean and hungry looking.' This brings a touching grin to Jim's lean and hungry face. Jim maybe is a very middle-aged sort of man; must have looked it already when he first joined the civil service. When he became a member of our club he was fiftyish, not fat but flabby, slack-jawed, and a very slow jogger. After five months he is still a slow jogger, but the flabbiness is going. He hangs around the more experienced runners looking for a kind word. Well, honestly, one can't compliment him on his speed, so we find this flattering comparison with Cassius 'lean and hungry', and he bounds off wagging his tail gratefully.'

36

How to Start

Now to set up some rules for strengthening beginners in their resolve to get to the end of those first few weeks. These rules can be embodied in the form of a basic schedule, but before that we must ensure that our beginner turns up on Day One.

Let's assume that you have been first enthused by watching the London Marathon and taken to heart that challenge 'If they can do it, why can't I?' Or someone has been uncomplimentary about the size of your belly, or you have just thrown away your twentieth cigarette with a curse.

At that very moment – the instant the whim seizes you – go out and do your first jog. Catch yourself in a weak moment.

Do not hesitate while you are looking out the correct fashionable running gear, or getting expert advice on heel and toe placing – leave immediately by the front door, go right round the block once and return home. Thousands actually do react like this; the moment the TV coverage of the London closes down you see people waddling along to the local park. I had an ecstatic letter one year from a woman in Evesham who said she'd gone straight out into the garden and done 70 laps, each of about 20 yards, round her ornamental apple tree. The dog was very upset about it all, but she'd logged her first mile!

I'd be obliged in fact if you'd stop reading right here and make your attempt this minute; see you later.

Be Gentle

Whatever you do on this first occasion, and over the next weeks, make sure you're being gentle with yourself. We don't want to lose you. It's a period in which to indulge yourself; in fact once you're up and into the schedule you ought to buy yourself a good pair of training shoes, if only because you then won't want to give up and see them left lurking in the cupboard, quite wasted.

Another tip: if it's stage fright that's stopping you, ask friends to come out with you: two or three of you together can bravely giggle back at the neighbours. This is how we had to deal with a woman friend, Linda Fazakerley, of Skipton, who failed three times in a row to set off on her maiden run. She had on a new tracksuit, new

Olympic racing shoes with half-inch spikes and a set of 'heavy-hands' but couldn't make it out of the front door. This was a person who was a regular parachutist, mind, and brave enough to push herself over the threshold at 3000 feet.

First she tried the 'urgent letter' treatment – when out running carry an envelope as if you're in a hurry to get it posted. Didn't work. Then rain-hood and dark glasses, a guaranteed impenetrable disguise. But no, she was sure she'd be recognised, if only by her big feet which she was very sensitive about as it was. So we went round to get her with a posse: four of us volunteered and allowed her to trot along half hidden in our 'rentacrowd'. Success!

What is needed is a confidence trick, to trick you into feeling confident. Find some big stimulation for yourself: repeat to yourself the various delicious benefits that you know running will bring, to take you past the brink. If you're a woman, remind yourself how running has swept the women of America; what's the matter with British women, you should bark at yourself, haven't we the enterprise? Show 'em!

Or find an outside motivation. Take advantage of some poor disabled group and get yourself sponsored on their behalf, collecting 50p from 20 acquaintances at the local. You'll oblige yourself to get that first run in, or you'll never feel able to enjoy another drink with them. And there's £10 riding on it for your favourite charity. Charities in Britain have made millions of pounds – actually millions – from runners in marathons getting themselves sponsored to provide an extra sharper challenge. This would be your first trial sponsorship. Linda Fazakerley actually had to do a weekly sponsorship for a while, to whip herself on stage by stage.

Once you have managed that first run, go out two or three times more just to feel relaxed, without worrying greatly about your actual time or distance run.

Now you may apply yourself to the schedule. Make allowances to suit your ability on the basis that the schedule is dedicated to the lowest common denominator, that chubby, former beauty queen from Southend, who once won all our hearts.

Anyone who fancies themselves a class above her may modify the programme accordingly, provided they don't overdo things in an access of impulsiveness.

Six Easy Weeks

Week 1 Should be carried out as advised above – no rules, just get into the open for a few minutes two or three times and enjoy yourself.

Week 2 A cautious opening to an improvement campaign. All you need by way of equipment is your plimsolls and half-a-dozen lamp-posts; lamp-posts happen to be planted apart at just about the required spacing. Use them as follows: Jog along to the first post, then fall back into a walk until the next, jog to the third, walk again and so on. If you need to walk for two spaces, do. A quarter of an hour altogether should do it, and you may take a mid-way rest if you wish. Do less if you feel bad, a little more if it is too easy. Some general rules: run on grass verges or sand rather than paving where it's possible, it's gentler on the ankles. But of course soft surfaces are not always accessible. Dress up more warmly than you might have planned, an extra vest is invaluable. Chilliness saps confidence. Keep your breathing going strongly; breathe *out* positively, breathing in will happen of its own accord.

In this second week, try to go out twice. Whether you train morning or evening or lunchtime or midnight is your own choice, some people's metabolism takes them one way, some the other.

Week 3 You should still be avoiding any measuring of your progress in terms of speed or distance; the object is to learn to feel easy moving along. Probably you are still walking the odd lamp-post length, but now you may be away from home for 20 minutes or so. Consider stopping half way to do some limbering up or stretching – or you could have started out at home with this.

Two or three times a week is ideal. And keep it fun, no straining.

Week 4 Make a move upwards now – try to extend your first jog a bit beyond the spot where you usually drop into a walk; soon attempt to discard the lamp-posts altogether, leaving them for the next beginner coming along. Three times a week by now.

You may have developed some minor stiffness in the calf or front of the thigh. Stiffness, like blisters, is not significant. It's not an injury. The treatment for it is a little more of what it took to make you stiff in the first place: the third or fourth time round it should massage itself away. The very act of jogging is the most excellent massage; it gets the blood going so that it gently swishes away the minute crystals of lactic acid in the muscles that bring on the 'pain' of stiffness.

Week 5 Any possibility of speeding up slightly to get that feeling of verve and vertigo, of swooping along on skis? Just for a few yards. It's a foretaste of what will come later, when I introduce hard training in the 'fartlek' mode. Fartlek is for those who perhaps enjoy the pleasanter aspects of masochism.

Week 6 This is simply the same run through again; it's to make certain one is able to spend 20 or 30 easy minutes in any sort of running, or running-and-walking. But there's no time limit; if you still find it tiring, sit through the course all over again, no extra charge. The object, remember, is to get you to the point where it's so rewarding that you can't drop out.

Once this is all securely behind us, we may look at long-range targets . . . . fun runs, racing, marathons and personal bests. We can also look forward with confidence to increasing fitness and a programme to help you remain young forever.

If the six easy weeks have been *too* easy, read on. You precocious muscular types must be separated off from run-of-the-mill beginners, or you become unbearable company.

5 A TOUGHER SIX WEEKS

If you're already reasonably fit – perhaps you're a regular tennis or squash player, or you kick an oval or round ball about – then the painstaking steps, the gently-cushioned schedule suggested for the self-conscious beauty queen now aged 45 will not be for you. You'd become bored and probably drop right out. Here is a more challenging introduction to running, with a little more variety to it. We set out a programme to ensure that you too become a committed runner and that at the end of the six weeks you're still with us.

Week 1 Probably you don't have difficulty in getting out for that first run – no doubt you are the type that sprints up the left hand side of escalators while all about you are taking a rest on the right hand side. So the most important thing to remember in your first week, nay your first run, is just to give yourself the taste of what it feels like. You know it is easy, your legs know it is easy – though your breathing might not be quite as sure – so leave yourself room for more. The idea is to come in from your runs rather like grandmother said you should rise up from the dinner table – hungry for more.

With your first week over, add just a little interest and variety. Interest comes from encouragement – encouragement from knowing that your pulse, your distance and your speed are improving, all of which come from extending yourself. Variety comes from change of place and pace. Perhaps it's a little early to introduce such refinements but I believe a little spice, a little challenge will keep you coming back for more.

From the very beginning you must take your pulse once a week, so equip yourself with a stop watch. Take the week as your unit and into it fit the pulse-reading, the number of runs you plan to do, the number of hills with the number of bursts or whatever. The basic measure is of the number of miles covered per week., (m.p.w.) It matters not whether you begin your week on Sunday or Monday. Some like to have their longest run over and done with early in the week so they start their running week on Sundays – a bit of mileage tucked under the belts makes them feel smug and unworried. Whereas others like to have Sunday at the end of the week, so that if their will and flesh has been a trifle weak during Monday through to Friday there's plenty of time to catch up at the end. It all depends what sort of person you are.

Week 2 At the end of one of your runs give yourself a feel of what a 50 yd sprint is like. Stretch out those legs and punch those arms. Don't stop suddenly though, run down gradually from such efforts. The heart is not too keen on sudden stops or starts. A warm-down after a hard effort is as important as a warm-up. And now is the time to get into the habit of stretching (See Chapter 12).

Week 3 Look for a new course offering variety: a flat course, an undulating course (known as 'bumpy' to the humorists), a scenic course. Remember it must be pleasurable as well as challenging. This is the week to set yourself up a course on which a time trial can be done, week by week, like the taking of your pulse. Work out a fixed course, starting perhaps at the first oak tree after the broken bench and finishing half a mile later at another fixed mark. (If you have a track nearby you can always run an accurate 800m or 1600m.) Mind you, if you *are* going to measure your times against the world's best, make it accurate. There's an old running track in Regents Park I know of where many a new runner has reported to me scintillating times – a sub 50 sec for a 400m or a sub 2.00m for an 800m. Imagine their disappointment when I had to report to them that the track is a little short – 60m infact!

However, the distance of your time trial course is not important. It is there as a measure to encourage you when you discover that you are quicker over that distance than you were a week or two ago. Take a note of your time on each occasion. In Week 3, too, you should be extending your runs.

Week 4 Introduce yourself to fartlek. 'Fartlek' means in Swedish 'go as you please'. Yes, go as you please, but try going a little faster

42

please. Not for long – maybe only for 50 yds or maybe 400 yds – but stretch out and get out of breath. When you are out of breath, slow down but don't stop; jog slowly until recovered. When you have recovered and feel sufficiently strong, off you go once more stretching those legs, using your arms, and trying to concentrate on breathing evenly. Recover. Another burst. Then the recovery. The training effect: improved capacity to take up and use oxygen.

To improve your running you must improve your capacity. So many runners stay 'one pace' runners all their careers because they don't teach their systems to maximise the possibilities. A person's body will only do what is expected of it, and if it is never expected to work a little harder and more efficiently it will protest loudly when first asked to do so. So once a week from now on do a bit of 'go as you please', whether it pleases you or not.

Week 5 Continue the good work but include a session over a hilly course. If you live in some such place as Norfolk, this might be hard. It is even harder if you are trying to train on an oil rig in the North Sea, as one fellow I know of has to do. But in these cases it is possible to improvise. In Norfolk you need just one incline, pretend it is a different hill each time you go up it. On an oil rig, try running up any stairs there may be! The idea is to learn to push yourself up hills using your arms and a higher leg lift. It is very important that you don't stop pushing until you are over the brow. Stop too early and you will find it much harder getting over the final hump. Push right to the top and over and you start recovering soon after you hit the top; your momentum carries you forward.

The ideal is a hilly course so that you can then treat it like a fartlek session where you might push up a hill repeatedly. Occasionally allow yourself a down-hill burst – not too often, as the jarring to the body and joints might lead to an injury. Then at the next hill try and fly up it to the top. Very strengthening if a little exhausting.

If it *is* in Norfolk, to get the training effect you will have to work out a circular course so that you hit the same hill several times. That's where you need to imagine it's a different hill each time. Failing that? Darn it, move to Somerset.

Week 6 This is the week to have a real go at your time trial. Make sure the day before is a rest day, avoid alcohol the evening before, sleep well, and concentrate. If you really want to be sure of a personal best time gather your friends to watch you flying fearlessly, there's nothing like an audience to make you perform. Better still race someone over the course. If fitter than you they will pull you along, if not you will discover new confidence as they struggle behind you. There is nothing like a bit of competition to pull that extra something out of you. After that – celebrate . . . . with a full hour's run.

So this is how your schedule might look:

Week 1: Mon   Run 10 minutes easy
           Wed   Run 12 minutes easy
           Sat   Run 20 minutes easy

Week 2: Mon   Run 20 minutes easy
           Wed   Run 15 minutes easy, ending with a burst and warm-down
           Thurs Run 20 minutes easy
           Sat   Run 30 minutes easy

Week 3: Mon   Run 20 minutes easy
           Wed   Run 30 minutes easy
           Fri   Run 20 minutes, including your first time trial
           Sun   Run 35 minutes easy

Week 4: Mon   Run 25 minutes easy
           Tues Run 35 minutes, including 'fartlek'
           Thurs Run 25 minutes easy
           Sat   Time trial, after warm-up, followed by warm-down – do it professionally
           Sun   Run 40 minutes easy

Week 5: Mon   Run 20 minutes easy
           Wed   Run 30 minutes, including some hills
           Thurs Run 25 minutes easy
           Sat   Run 25 minutes, including time trial
           Sun   Run 45 minutes

44

Week 6: Mon   Run 20 minutes
         Wed   Run 40 minutes, including some 'fartlek'
         Thurs Run 10 minutes
         Sat   Time trial, rent-a-crowd to make sure
         Sun   Run 50 minutes or 60 minutes in celebration.

Remember, a schedule is not rigid, you must learn what you are capable of, how far you can push yourself, how far you can't. Be flexible. If you're tired, cut down; if it's too easy increase a little. The art of running is to find your level, to find what you run best on – some go for mileage and some for quality. At the end of six weeks you should start to consider what suits you best. Try building up mileage and if after a while you find that it leaves you constantly tired, try more quality work – fartlek, hills, and so on – over fewer miles. Everybody is different. To improve you must now begin to analyse your strengths and your weaknesses. It is a fascinating piece of research which can give you insight into what makes you tick and what makes others tick.

By the seventh week you are now serious . . . . so investigate a club, if you haven't already. Why? Read on.

6   TIME TO JOIN A CLUB

Once you're regularly into running, you've become a member of the world's greatest club, four or five million members in Britain, hundreds of millions all over the world, and you've paid your foundation membership fee with those first formidable weeks of effort. That is the time to think about joining a club in actuality.

There is no need to feel you have to be an 'athlete' to be welcomed into a club. There's room for all styles, all ages and all abilities in the traditional local athletics club, raw beginners as well as national heroes. In addition special clubs for joggers and for veterans have been established these past few years; you may belong to all three types together if you wish, quite a privilege.

Whatever you want out of running, be it fitness, competition or good company, is best found inside a club. The club is there for the benefit of the members, who may shamelessly help themselves to what they want; club members are takers not givers. This does not necessarily appeal to the oppressed and overworked committee members, but that's how it always is. Those in administration have taken it on for the glory, after all, not only for the good they're doing. Typically, out of a club of 500 members there are no more than a dozen who get things done and they are happy enough that the rest of the 500 do them the honour of turning out to run.

You therefore have a licence to take it quite selfishly, to use the club to improve your running, and to extract any other values you may from it.

What are these values? Take the practical items first: you have a place to run, measured and marked out probably, with changing facilities if you need them, refreshments often enough, and a rendezvous where you may meet your training mates.

More to the point are the social and psychological benefits. Today's long-distance runner is no longer lonely, but the most gregarious of characters, for it is after all of considerable value to a runner to build up a network of acquaintances of like levels of performance with whom to compare experience.

It is helpful to be provided with running mates for training days, and above all it is good to have training support when you are low. On your own a low patch makes you want to chicken out of your run; with a club you know there are people relying on you, who will in turn help you through the first hard half mile – amazing how easy any run becomes once you have stepped out on the trail. Joining a club is all benefits and no obligations; even that obligation to your clubmates to be there, is basically a boon to yourself.

For the small annual membership fee, often less than £10, you have the whole club structure open to you; training opportunities right through the year; the club's own race events right through the year; information about other events, advice and coaching and usually the prerogative to buy running gear at the club discounts. The club is for everyone. To stay outside it is to handicap yourself. In a club your running will flourish.

It becomes a sheltered community for the timid and a stepping stone for the brave. It can be the centre for fitness or for racing; the place to build up your physique or hang up your trophies. The great Baron de Coubertin might have said that for every runner it is not merely winning but being part of the club that counts.

Once you are a veteran – the age groups begin at 35 for women and 40 for men – you'd be advised to join a vets club. In a vets club you will find yourself among your peers, and thus more likely to track down appropriate solutions to problems of injury, training and so on for the older runner. There also is the place to locate competition at a suitable level, where one will not be always outclassed by the fit and young. To be outclassed in every race is to lose heart and not give of one's best.

I'm a firm believer in the value of competition, in fact the definite need for it. It does everyone good, drawing more effort out of the runner, to bring yet higher levels of fitness – even for those who run purely to keep fit there is value in entering a race.

I have met many runners who deny quite categorically that they are at all competitive and wish nothing more of life than to do their comfortable 3 miles of an evening. Yet, when I have finally persuaded them to try a low-profile fun run, say, they end up appreciating the extra enjoyment brought them . . . . teased out of them by being in contention with some stranger up the last long slope. And at the tape, at the end of the race, that is when they experience that delightful euphoria, the runner's high.

How to Join

In the next chapters will be more on competition, hard and easy; here now is information about how to join a club, whether one of the 1,500 clubs in Britain affiliated to the AAA, one of the local joggers' clubs, or a veteran's club.

The Athletic Clubs

These are the backbone of the whole athletics system and scene in this country and the envy of other nations, including the USA, which relies mainly on its university network. Many of our great clubs were formed a century or more ago, in the hare and hounds days. Today they cater for road running and cross-country, as well as the whole range of track and field. Their membership is open to young and old, men and women, world class and village class, and takes in many a family – father, mother, colt and girl.

To find your local club ask at libraries, leisure centres, sports shops or town halls, or stop a group out running and jog alongside them long enough to ask them where they hail from. In the final resort you can contact either the Sports Council or the Athletic Association. Here are the telephone numbers of their regional offices.

Sports Council
North: Durham 49595;
North West: 061-834 0338;
Yorks/Humberside: Leeds 436443;
East Midlands:
Nottingham 821887;
West Midlands: 021-454 3808;
East: Bedford 45222;
Greater London/South East: 01-778 8600;
South: Reading 595616;

Athletic Associations
London 828-9326
Southern Counties: 01-828 8640;
Midland Counties: 021-773 1631;
Northern Counties: 051-708 9363;
Women's AAA: 01-828 4731;
Wales: 0222-396614 (men);
0446-743126 (women);
Scotland 031-226 4401;
Northern Ireland: 0232-661222
    (men);

South Wales: Crewkerne 73491;   0232-704891 (women).
Scotland: Edinburgh 2258411;
Wales: Cardiff 397571;
Northern Ireland: Belfast 663154.

The New Breed Club

Formed from the new wave running converts, these clubs exist
alongside the AAA structure and many of them are now actually
affiliated to the official body. They started as ad hoc groups such as
the Burnham Joggers, the Feltham Puffers, the Centurion
Joggers, the Steel City Striders, got together to compete in the
early *Sunday Times'* Fun Runs and such events, and gradually
became strong and established – nevertheless their first duty is still
to the hopeful beginner.

To find your own Local Lopers keep an eye on advertisements in
magazines – or wait in ambush for a likely member in the park. It's
not impossible either that a call to the AAA will point you in the
right direction.

If you still can't find a way in, enter the next *Sunday Times* run,
where you should certainly be able to pick up the scent.

The Veteran Clubs

Everyone of age should join a vets club no matter whether
already a member of one of the other types. To be affiliated to the
vets is the only way in to specific vets races – and there are
hundreds of such events in the year, local, regional, national, and
international. The clubs put on every sort of run for every sort of
runner, from the 100m to the marathon, for men and women,
starting at 35 and going on for ever. Races are held on the track, on
the road and across the country. There is also team competition,
which means that even the slow runners can find themselves
much-valued members of their club.

In these races you might find yourself shoulder to shoulder – for
a few yards, at any rate – with famed champions of the past, such as
Ron Hill, Christopher Brasher, Judy Vernon, John Disley, or with
quite unrated beginners. The events are always seeded into five-
year age groups, so that at every stage each runner has some chance
of success, or at any rate is not ruled out purely on the grounds of

49

age. Even in the Over 70s there is competition for such as Jenny Wood Allen of Dundee. In the Over 80s there is still tough contention between men like Ron 'Chalky' White, E. Daley, Bob Roberts and others of the VAC, most of whom have been active members of that club since the 1940s. To keep on running is to keep on living.

To find a vets club, contact the secretary of the organisation nearest to you from the list below. (Note you may join more than one club, if you wish to double up your range of competition.)

Area Secretary

Midlands: Alf Sparkes
2 William Bullocks Close
New Street
Stourport-on-Severn
Worcs.

North: Ron Cooper
75 Bluebell Avenue
Penistone
Sheffield S30 6AF

South: Jack Heywood
14 Darling Road
London SE4 IYQ

East: E.C. Butcher
26 Rycroft Avenue
Deeping St. James
Peterborough PE6 8NT

VAC (*Mainly London Area*)
Peter Harvey
51 Buckingham Way
Wallington, Surrey

Scotland: Henry Muchamore
5 Templedean Park
Haddington
East Lothian EH0I 3ND

Wales: Tom Wood
              50 St Julians Avenue
              Newport
              Gwent

Isle of Man: Brian Doughty
              Seaview Cottage
              Port St Mary
              Isle of Man

N. Ireland: W. Brannigan
              3 Somerset Avenue
              Bangor
              Co. Down
              N. Ireland BT20 3BQ

Women's Veterans:
              Miss B. Cushen
              156 Mitcham Road
              West Croydon, Surrey
              (Note: Women may join an area club as well as the
              Women Vets AC).

Every Club Has Its Own Story

In which our author discovers the VAC . . . . How he attempts to make
contact . . . . Of the cold reception he meets . . . . How Mike McDowell's help is enlisted . . . . The intervention of a Heatwave . . . . and a
Rolls Royce . . . . The subsequent winning over of the Wellings . . . .
The final happy thereafters.

I've no doubt that the best move I ever made myself was to join a
club.In those days, however, at the start of the 1970s it was not so
simple. A 50-year-old beginner was not what every club wanted; at
the ordinary Amateur Athletic Association club you were expected
to have become an official, out in all weathers with a stopwatch,
long before you turned 50! And the only veterans' club in existence
at that time was exceedingly exclusive.

51

It took me time to track it down. Until then my running had been carried on at family picnics; seeing how well I handled the younger generation I thought how splendid it would be if only there were an Olympics for the Over 40s, or at least some platform for older runners to get together regularly. I then chanced on the Veterans' Athletic Club in London. At last! But they were rather cool in response. A club was a club, they had their quota of members, and who was I? They were a *club*, not a *movement*, that's how they saw it.

I pressed the point through and was duly, if rather grudgingly taken on strength. From that day endless richness flowed for me.

Rather fancifully I came to feel that out of the crucible of the VAC arose the world running boom, too, creating riches in the same way for the rest of the world. Without their realising it, without their wanting it even, the VAC and its long-serving secretary, Arthur Welling, *had* started a movement.

So, to tell the story of the VAC is to tell the story of the running boom.

The club was founded in 1931; thereafter its example and influence led, post-war, to a seeding of the veteran running movement in the US, Australia, Canada and New Zealand, as well as in the rest of the UK and Europe.

In the US it grew fast. Its veteran members (known as masters there) were key figures in touching off the world-wide road running explosion . . . . James Fixx in his best-selling books, Dr Kenneth Cooper in his, Dr George Sheehan in his *Runners' World* articles, Alison Ullyot in hers.

But back in Britain the VAC was still pursuing its quiet old ways. At the time I joined I found the club ruled by a committee that had been in power for years, and it in turn was ruled by Arthur. There was also to be taken into account the power behind the throne, Mrs Welling. Whoever found her favour, found Arthur's.

And whoever would lead this charming lady round the dance floor at the club's annual dinner was already half-way there.

Arthur was a rugged-looking man, not your distinguished senatorial type. Instead of smooth silvery hair, he had a bristly crop of the stuff. A retired railway worker, he lived in a terrace of small cottages south of Wimbledon.

He ran the club by the rule book. An old product of the amateur movement, he never deviated from AAA rules of track and cross-country competition. The latest copy of the regulations was kept in his cricket bag, capacious enough to hold not only his own running gear but the race paraphernalia, including a specially manufactured metre marker. This was a hinged, wooden affair, with a piece of chalk on one end, like an oversized pair of compasses. An hour before every handicap race Arthur would be down at the grounds, marking off the number of metres the handicapping committee had allotted each runner as his start. It was all accurate and formal.

As an ex-railwayman he was able to get himself to and from the grounds free if he went by rail, though this often meant arriving an hour or two earlier than necessary depending on the week-end train time-table. He would twirl his compasses around to chalk a mark on the side of the track where each man was to set off. 'Spot on!' he would announce.

Arthur's talk marked him out as one who had been in his prime during World War Two: 'Gone for a Burton', 'On your bike', 'Had it'. Nevertheless he was a man of great vitality of language, witty in his daily speech and remarkable when addressing a public gathering – it was Arthur's orations at the annual dinner-dances that made them the great and rewarding occasions they were, especially for the non-dancers. He could make a point with tremendous timing, a wise wink and a choice phrase – a phrase that was always very much spot on.

By the beginning of the 1970s that American jogging wave had rolled forward mightily, and now began to be felt back in Britain. But paradoxically it immediately came smack up against a wall. The traditional club runner wanted to have nothing to do with the members of this new breed and certainly the veterans and vets clubs of London, the North and Scotland, were agin it all.

Who wanted a running boom? The old runners were a thoroughly dour type . . . . who needed any new-fangled new wave?

More particularly who needed a new breed of runners that happened to be mostly middle-class, flashing money about, wearing trendy running kit – and driving slick cars, not using public transport. Diabolical!

So Arthur Welling and the VAC were against the boom as such. Thus it was that when the 40 and 50-year-olds among the new breed came along to join the vets club they found no eager welcome at all. Poor fellows, even at 38 or 39 they had started looking forward to becoming part of this movement!

The subject of their joining was first gone over in committee. The senior members were all very critical of the style of the new applications for membership. 'They don't know the rules, even,' sniffed the Chief Timekeeper.

'Last Saturday there's two of 'em arguing with me about their handicaps,' complained the Club Starter. 'Arguing the bleeding toss!'

'I'll tell you another thing, my lads: they got more money than they got sense.' So the judgement of Arthur Welling from the chair. 'Carry around three or four pair of spare shoes under their arm, like they was Rod Laver.'

Observed the Timekeeper further: 'With these kind it's all flash in the pan, get them into the club and give them a hand-up, six months later they're gorn off to join something else – climbing the North Pole prob'ly'.

'I been a member of this club nineteen years continuous, Mr Chairman,' put in the Leading Ultra Runner primly at this point.

'Mr Chairman,' piped up another Roadrunner, 'you don't *climb* the North Pole. There's no actual pole, they found.'

'Order! Order!' bellowed Arthur giving the Timekeeper the floor again.

He got to his feet: 'Is there any call we got to make it easy for these new twisters?' he asked.

'Right, sport, you got it spot on,' cried Arthur. 'No spoon-feeding!' He jabbed his finger truculently at the list of applicants. 'No need to spoon-feed 'em.'

That sized up the feeling of the meeting. No spoon-feeding – the policy was adopted immediately, nem con. They could hardly refuse perfectly respectable applicants, but there was no law that they had to make it easy for them.

Arthur and the Timekeeper set up a two-man inquisition among the hopeful new recruits. 'What's your previous club?' asked the Timekeeper of one, knowing quite well he had none.

'What's your best time for 10 mile, mate?' Arthur enquired of other recruits sceptically.

'Who proposed you for membership?' the Timekeeper continued in the same suspicious vein.

In spite of these delaying tactics though, a few of the new breed managed to work their way into the club, and two of us, Mike McDowell and myself, actually got onto the committee in due course.

'You'd be 'aving a go at the Four Minute Mile now, no doubt?' Arthur put to Mike ironically. In fact Mike was a real runner, a 5,000m man, and a long-time member of Ranelagh Harriers, but otherwise he was to be sure middle-class, chairman of a big international engineering concern, and with a smart private address in South London. Far worse though – positively despicable – he drove a Rolls Royce!

Right away the two of us put our foot in it. For a start we both toured with the British team that went over to Toronto for the first ever vets international, or 'World Masters', whereas Arthur and his cronies stayed at home, suspicious of this new internationalism and anyway not finding it so easy to shell out for the expenses of a transatlantic junket.

Then, in our innocence, we got so enthused with all this great new running movement, Mike and I, that we immediately put up a resolution in committee calling for all sorts of improvements to club facilities. In order to finance these projects we suggested raising the annual membership dues.

'After all,' I claimed naïvely, 'the subs are only 25p.'

'How much?' rasped Arthur after a long pause while pretending to be preoccupied with the minutes book.

'Only 25p,' I bleated.

'Five bob,' Arthur corrected me, pointing his pencil aggressively right at my nose, 'five bob mate.' It seemed a lot more money putting it this way.

We pressed the point, however, McDowell and myself.

What was the need for all these fancy improvements, the committee wanted to know? Everything was quite satisfactory, as it had been for years.

'The subs was the same when I first joined eleven years ago as what they is now, Mr Chairman,' announced Roadrunner. (Eleven years of inflation!)

'What about the OAPs' asked another member accusingly, 'How they going to pay more?'

'And I been a member nineteen years,' followed up the Ultra-

55

Man just to put the record straight again. 'Yus, nineteen years continuous.'

Arthur summed up the sentiment of the committee. He put it directly to us! 'What's the reason for all this spending malarky?'

Now Mike and I felt we could come out with our big argument, and pull victory out of the hat. 'To get more people running, attract more members!'

What a buzz of reaction with a very disapproving tone to it.

'Order!' was shouted from the chair.

'Order, order!' was shouted from the floor.

Arthur took it on himself to lay it on the line to the two of us. 'Ere Buster,' he said to Mike, looking around the corner of his nose at him through a belligerent eye, ''ang on, mate! You tell me what you want new members for.'

'Yes, we got plenty enough members,' hollered the Club Starter.

The backwoodsmen began to pile in too, while the Timekeeper showed grave signs of putting forward a resolution.

Neither Arthur nor the membership of the club, it appeared, were interested in spreading the movement of running just for the glory of it. They had a club, it was their club and what did they want any more members for?

That turned out to be typical of what went on all over Britain. Just as our own VAC's influence had originally spread throughout the country and then overseas, setting veterans everywhere running, now we became the influence that barred progress; our fellow dogs-in-the-manger in the rest of England and in Scotland set themselves against the new breed too and formed a log jam against the modern current.

That is until the day of the club 10 mile championships, when at last the current began to press through.

Everything went wrong at this race, held on the asphalt paths of Richmond Park in a large figure of eight. First of all, although it was only May, the park was crowded with cars gawping at the deer, edging the runners quite thoughtlessly over into the verges. It was unexpectedly fine weather that had brought them out. In fact the weather served up that day was a full and fierce heatwave, the only conditions that the long distance man ever fears. By the end of the race no less than a dozen of the competitors finished distressed, or – most unusual for such a group of hard-bitten old runners – they did not finish at all.

Between them these competitors must have turned out in ten thousand races over their lifetimes and never experienced such an indignity before.

There was real worry about the condition of some of the older men. Arthur and I – both being sprinters, we took no part in these road races – tried to look after our exhausted comrades but finally we had to send for an ambulance for two men, one of them a national hero of a generation before over the middle distances.

At the same time, however, we had to see to the official running of the race – the show must go on! So how useful it was when Mike McDowell, having run his race, was able to transport these two worst cases off to casualty, no ambulance as yet having been contacted. And of course he bore them grandly away in his Rolls!

A valuable service. The Club Starter and many another made a point of thanking him personally. In presenting the trophies after the race even Arthur deigned to make a special mention of this friendly act, what's more wangling for Mike a special handicap prize. 'Well done, mate!'

Then as we were preparing to pack up and depart, word went out of an injury in the Welling ranks. Now what could this be? Arthur, as mentioned, had not been competing. Well, it was Mrs Welling, who had turned an ankle and was quite unable to hobble the mile to the nearest public transport. On many an occasion before had Arthur stalwartly refused a lift from the debonair McDowell, but this time things were different.

McDowell stepped forward courteously and the Wellings were handed into the back of his car, with rather gruff thank-yous. It wasn't altogether easy bundling in Mrs Welling, a large lady, but it was nicely done.

Mike drove at a stately speed over to their suburban terrace road, to draw up right in front of their cottage. He now took a chauffeur's cap out of the cubby-hole where his official driver normally stowed it, crammed it on his head, sprang out of the car, opened the back door with a flourish and handed the Wellings out in the grandest of manners, standing at the salute as they walked from the Rolls to their front steps and into the house.

The neighbours watched and cheered.

That was the first breakthrough in the affairs of the club. What could Arthur Welling do but admit Mike McDowell to the ranks of humanity? The establishment was tottering . . . .

Then at the annual club dance, by which time Mrs Welling was quite recovered and looking forward to her annual big treat, the final act was played out. This time Arthur was the injured one – 'Done me hamstring,' he complained, rubbing the back of his thigh and turning on a very fine limp.

Who would take Mrs Welling through an evening of two-steps, slow foxtrots and waltzes? One or two of the party came forward to make the chivalrous attempt, but they quite failed.

Whereupon up stepped Mike McDowell, to take her by the hand and whirl that large but basically nimble lady around the dance floor to her complete satisfaction.

Her evening was saved, and so was Arthur's, who wrung Mike's hand in gratitude and congratulations, as if he had at last indeed brought off the Four Minute Mile. Over the cheery round face of Mrs Welling was wreathed the Four Minute Smile!

That is how the running boom was finally helped into Britain. Arthur and his cronies immediately put up the club subscription fee to a full £1, used the proceeds to set up a number of splendid new races and invited in all and sundry. Soon enough the club membership list stood at just under the 1,000 and other vets clubs followed suit.

By the time that Chris Brasher established his London Marathon there was a catchment area of thousands of veteran runners to swell the ranks. Year by year they contributed a large and growing percentage to the marathon entry statistics and to the boom generally – about a third of all Britain's runners today are veterans.

Arthur himself died in his seventieth year, alas, but he had seen the first of the big London marathons, and seen VAC members win many a medal in the veterans' sections of the race.

Subsequently Mike McDowell was made president of the club for a term of honour and at national level the various veterans clubs joined together to form a sustaining network for the tens of thousands of runners, old breed and new, men and now also women, who constitute the British Vets.

7 RACE TRAINING

Competition turns a new runner into a fanatic. After your first two or three runs you're in its unforgiving grip and ready to devote yourself to the racing life.

As a zealot, your first task is to adapt your training specifically to this new vocation. You need to have your life carefully scheduled, week by week, with up-and-coming races in mind.

To provide you with a set of classic training schedules I sought the advice of the Wise Man of Running, who was running barefoot and winning races long before Zola Budd was born, Bruce Tulloh.

An international 5000m gold medallist, one-time coach for the Kenyan track team, record breaking coast-to-coast runner across America, Tulloh in his 40s became one of the famous regulars of the *Sunday Times* Fun Run and an advisor to the millions training for the mass marathons.

Bruce told me he believes that general training principles apply equally to vets: regular training which, very gradually, increases the quantity and quality of the workload as the runner builds towards the goal race. 'There are two ways in which a vet differs from a younger runner,' Bruce told me. '*First*, he doesn't seem to have the same sense of urgency about achieving certain targets. Maybe it's a sort of maturity, but the vet runner does tend to take the longer view. And that is a good thing. *Second*, they can do as much training at 45 as at 25, but they are more prone to injury, and recovery takes longer.'

Bearing these two things in mind, here are Bruce's recommendations, which are based on the principle of interval training. They give best results at all distances.

'Novices,' says Bruce, 'should introduce bursts against the clock during their steady weekday runs. For instance, after 10 minutes of steady running, you could do one minute fast, two minutes slow, repeating the pattern about six times before doing a steady

10-minute jog as a warm-down. As you get fitter, you can shorten the recovery to one minute, then to 30 seconds. And then do track intervals.' Your track doesn't need to be the top class international facility like Crystal Palace or Edinburgh, but can be simply a grass track in your local park – all that is really needed is a regular measured distance that can be run at a faster than normal pace.

Bruce then noted down for me three specific schedules, tougher than what you will have done before, planned to callous your mind and body to accept hardship when you are racing.

The first of the training schedules is a build-up programme to get you used to that hardened approach. The second is a basic six-week schedule to repeat ad infinitum; it allows you to race regularly while ensuring that you get in enough hard training weeks to improve your times. The third schedule is more mileage biased. It is designed for the mighty marathon.

All three schedules have in common the interval sessions. The idea of interval training is simple: by adjusting one of a number of variables, you make each subsequent one more demanding (or demanding in a different way) than the previous one. The variables are: distance of the repetitions: speed or pace of the repetitions; quantity of the repetitions; and time of the recovery.

For example, you might go along to your local track to run six times 400 metres (6×400m in the shorthand version) and complete those efforts in 67,71,76,78,81 and 76 seconds, taking various amounts of rest in between each effort.

But that is of no value. Each recovery period *must* be the same (probably about 90sec for beginners), and all your 400m times should be as close together as possible – in this case, nearer to the 75sec average the runner was able to achieve.

Of course, you can achieve different things in interval sessions, depending on your objectives. If you want to run a really quick 800m on the track, then a session of three or four really fast 300-metre repetitions with a generous recovery (2 minutes) could be useful to improve your speed. Or you could try an 'acceleration session', where you run, say, 400m, with a definite 'kick' acceleration injected over the final 150 metres on each of your six repetitions. Or you might be training to complete a 4-hour marathon. That requires you to run at just outside 9-minute miles for the full distance. What you could do is, on a 10 or 13 mile run, throw in three or four one-mile efforts, trying to run at 8½-minute mile pace, and give yourself a 5-minute jog recovery between each effort. In that fashion, you will gradually accustom yourself to the demands of 9-minute-miling – that can be achieved by either increasing the number of 'fast' miles that you run or by reducing the breaks in between, until you are virtually running each effort mile back-to-back.

Bruce, after being a top class competitive athlete for many years, admits that the instinct and urge to prove himself is no longer as strong as in his younger days. 'And I've noticed that the same is true for a number of other international athletes who were around at my time,' he says. 'But then there are others, new runners, who are as competitive within the veteran category as they probably would have been in the open age group twenty years before.' One example of such keen newcomers that spring to mind is a Highgate Harrier clubmate of mine, Robin Dow. Robin left school in 1962 and did no running for nearly twenty years. No exercise for Robin, just a life of fags and booze. Until, that is, four weeks before a gruelling 30-kilometre cross-country race in Sweden in 1981, when he volunteered to run to make up a company team. When he finished, he felt like 'a piece of pulp', but also realised that he had a bit of talent for running. On five weeks' training before the 1982 London Marathon, Robin managed to finish in 3:06. Now he began to take running seriously, and a year later, aged 39, he improved his time sensationally to 2:22:54. Today Robin is one of the leading British veteran runners; he trains with all the seriousness and application you would expect from some Olympic athlete.

As Bruce Tulloh says, 'The similarities between vets and younger runners are greater than the differences – after all, a fit runner is a fit runner, regardless of age.' Follow the training schedule, and gradually develop *your* fitness . . . .

Build-up schedule

In this training programme note the use of the word 'pace'. You should determine your mile pace, 3,000m pace and 5,000m pace. If you can run 5,000m in 18 minutes, that means each lap should be run in 86sec in the race – therefore a session performed at 5,000m pace should have 800m reps. run in 2:50 (just inside flat 86s, to give it a bit of edge!) For road runs a formula of *Race Pace* (RP)+so many seconds. First you need to determine what distance race is your target event – obviously your race pace for 10km is going to be quicker than your marathon race pace. Let us consider an example where you want to run a half-marathon in 90min. Such a time requires 6:52 mile pace to be maintained throughout the race. Therefore 'RP+30sec' suggests that for a particular run, you should complete each mile in around 7:22. Similarly, if you are tasked to run 'RP–15sec', then you should try to maintain 6:37 miles throughout the training session.

Week 1
6M hilly run at RP+30sec
4M fast run at RP–15sec
8M road intervals – 4×2min efforts with 3min recoveries
10m at RP+60sec

Week 2
6M steady at RP+30sec
6 hill sprints
8M road intervals – 8×1min with 2min recoveries
12M at RP+60sec

Week 3
8M hilly at RP+30sec
6M steady at RP+30sec
7M fartlek
Road Race – 10km or 10M

Week 4
8M steady at RP+30sec
4M easy at RP+60sec
8M fartlek
Intervals – 10×400m (or 80sec) at 3,000m pace, with 1min recoveries
10M steady at RP+30sec

Week 5
5M fast at RP–15sec
6M hilly at RP
8M road intervals – 5×3min with 2min recoveries
13M steady at RP+60sec

Week 6
8M steady at RP+30sec
10 hill sprints
6M fartlek
Intervals – 10×300m (or 60sec) at 3,000m pace, with 30sec recoveries
15M steady at RP+60sec

Week 7
6M hilly at RP
8M fartlek
Intervals – 10×200m (30sec) at 3,000m RP with 1min recoveries
Road Race – 10Km or less

Week 8
10M steady at RP+15sec
6M fartlek
8M road intervals – 3×6min, 6min recoveries
6M steady at RP+15sec
13M steady at RP+30sec

Week 9
8M hilly at RP+30sec
8M fartlek
Intervals – 12×300m at 1,500m pace with 1min recoveries
15M steady at RP+60sec

Week 10
10M steady at RP+10sec
12 hill sprints
6M steady at RP+30sec
Interval – 12×400m at 3,000m pace with 30sec recoveries
16M steady at RP+45sec

Week 11
6M at RP−15sec
6M fartlek
6M steady at RP+15sec
Intervals − 10×200m at 1,500m pace with 90sec recoveries
Road Race − 10m-half-marathon

Week 12
8M at RP+30sec
12 hill sprints
8M fartlek
Intervals − 6×600m at 3,000m pace with 2min recoveries
16M steady at RP+30sec

The racer's schedule

This consists of six weeks' training, with two road races during that period, which can be repeated in order as a regular training schedule, allowing you to compete at distances of 10km to the half-marathon and to continue improving. Aspiring marathon runners should undertake this schedule before going on to the marathon programme.

Week A
6M steady at RP+15sec
Intervals − 10×400m at 1,500m pace with 2min recoveries
Road intervals (8M in total) − 5×6min with 3min recoveries
12 hill sprints
18M steady at RP+60sec

Week B
10M steady at RP+30sec
Intervals − 12×300m at 1,500m pace with 1min recoveries
6M fartlek
6M steady at RP+30sec
6M fartlek
Race − 10km

Week C
6M fartlek
10M at RP+10sec
Intervals – 6×800m at 5,000m pace (accelerate over last 200s) with 2min recoveries
8M steady at RP
15M steady at RP+30sec

Week D
6M steady at RP
Intervals – 15×200m at 1,500m pace with 1min recoveries
10M hilly at RP+15sec
6M fartlek
4M easy (say RP+60sec)
Road Race – half-marathon or longer (up to 20M)

Week E
6M steady at RP+30sec
Intervals – (200,400,600,800,600,400,200)×2 at 3,000m pace, with 90 sec recoveries
6M fartlek
8M steady at RP
15M steady – 10M at RP+30sec, final 5M at RP–15sec

Week F
4M easy (say RP+60sec)
Intervals – 4×1,000m at 5,000m pace with 3min recoveries
10M steady at RP
6M fartlek
8M steady – 6M at RP+30sec, 2M at RP–30sec
17M steady at RP+30sec

Marathon Schedule

After following the last two schedules through at least once each, you should be ready for a marathon in six weeks – all you need is the following schedule, aimed at steadily increasing your stamina.

Week G
6M fartlek
Intervals – 12×400m at 1,500m pace with 90sec recoveries
10M hilly at RP+15sec
8M road intervals – 5×6min with 2min recoveries
4M at RP+30sec
8M steady at RP+15sec
18M steady at RP+30sec

Week H
4M at RP+30sec
Intervals – 15×300m at 1,500m pace with 60sec recoveries
10M at RP–15sec
15 hill sprints
6M fartlek (very easy)
Half-marathon race

Week J
8M fartlek – very much longer efforts
Intervals – 8×600m at 1,500m pace with 2min recoveries
10M hilly at RP+30sec
10M road intervals – 4×12min efforts with 5min recoveries
8M steady at RP+30sec
20M steady at RP+30sec (faster, if possible, over last 4M)

Week K
4M at RP+30sec
Intervals – (200,400,600,800,1000,800,600,400,200)×2 at 5,000m
pace with 2min recoveries
6M fartlek
15 hill sprints
Intervals – 6×400m at 1,500m pace but accelerating over last 200s.
1min recoveries
8M steady at RP–15sec
20M steady – 15M at RP+30sec, 5M at RP–10sec

Week L
4M easy at RP+30sec
Intervals – 6×800m at 1,500m pace with 2min recoveries

8M fartlek
15M fast (after 2M warm-up) at RP–60sec
8M steady at RP+15sec
15M steady at RP+15sec

Week M
Intervals – 10×200m at 3,000m pace with 1min recoveries
6M steady at RP+15sec
4M easy fartlek

Now the Marathon!

8   RUNNING TO WIN

This is for you if you want to be winning medals and accolades
. . . . if you're ambitious . . . . adventurous . . . . seeking to
extract the very best from yourself.

If you want to improve, it takes work, but you *can* do better.
You have years of racing before you, in which to extend yourself.

To do well in races you must of course set out determined. But to
sparkle in a race you must set out to win, you must act like a star.
The stars know intuitively how to prepare, when to experiment,
when to assert themselves, when to gamble . . . . Here are nine rules
to keep you thinking like a star so that perhaps you become one.

Rule no. 1: Be prepared. Prepare for your races by psyching up.
You psyche up by running the race over in your head beforehand,
by learning as much about your opposition as you can and by
acquainting yourself with the course in advance. Particularly
check where the finish is so that you can make your final bid.
Decide in advance not to be unsettled by wind or hills – only
mediocre racers let that happen. After all, everyone is going to be
handicapped in the same way. Don't worry about your opposition,
it could just be that today they are under par or, better, that you've
improved since last you raced them.

Know roughly what splits you should be aiming for and remind
yourself of your errors or your successes in your last race.

Say the race is a 10K, the pre-race scenario in your head might go
something like this: 'Go out strongly . . . . concentrate on settling
in . . . . use George to take me out . . . . remember not to worry if
my first split turns out too fast . . . . dig in between 2K and 7K
. . . . time to really concentrate . . . . try to pick up pace by using
upper body . . . . finish line in sight – go hard for the line, stretch
out legs and punch the arms . . . . don't be overtaken on run in.'

Rule no. 2: Have no preconceptions. Until you work out your formula for success, do not trap yourself with set ideas about the type of runner you are. Why have preconceptions such as 'I don't like running in hot weather' or 'I never do well in that particular race'. It does make life easier, doesn't it? Yet you might be feeling terrific on the day. So make up your mind to test your theories about yourself and discover if they are really true. Yes, you may not really be a slow developer, just lazy and uncourageous.

Feeling tired before a race can sometimes be a trick of the mind. More often than not once the gun goes you settle into the race to discover you're not tired at all. You were only fooling yourself. Of course if you are really tired then your race time will show it. And if this is the case then you must start asking 'why am I tired?' It might be that you need a rest.

Rule no. 3: Learn to rest. There is the seasonal, planned rest and the forced rests from exhaustion. For the seasonal you must plan ahead – sometimes as much as a year. Plan which races to peak for. You might want to be at your best for the European Veterans Championships in the summer. So plan to build up strength and endurance over cross-country the winter before, graduating to speed work in April, using open meetings and championships for sharpening up.

But prior to all this take a break from the last season. Get away from running altogether for a week or two. Do anything else: go swimming, walking, canoeing – but don't run. Really enjoy yourself then you will be raring to go when you restart.

Learn to take unplanned rests, too. If you become dispirited by training and racing results, it's probably because of over-training and over-racing. If you feel really tired take a day off. If you are sickening for 'flu, rest until you are completely better. A week lost now is better than four later. Don't panic about training schedules. Training when tired is of little value. To know when to rest is an art.

Rule no. 4: Don't be negative. Accentuate the positive. Half the battle is believing. Don't put negative thoughts into your head about blowing up – otherwise you will. Don't think about taking things easy – in which case you'll lose a chance. Step out in your running and you will step out in your life.

Rule no. 5: Experiment. During your next races try to do things differently. Go out fast in one of them to see what really happens. Surprise yourself. You might just strike gold by doing so. If by going out too fast you spoil your race accept that the experiment failed. Then either *train* to cope with a fast opener or learn to pace yourself just right. Perhaps you are the slow developer, but do you really develop in the second half? After a mile or two you should be warmed up and ready to go. If you find it hard to step up then – conclude that you're not the late developing type.

Experiment in training too. There isn't one formula that works for everyone, so find the best one for you through trial and error. That is what successful training is about. Find the training method that suits you. Read up the subject, learn from what others do and say. Adapt methods to maximise your potential.

Experiment with modes of running. Style again is a very individual thing, and most people should be allowed to run as they run, but it might be worth doing some research on yours. Are your shoulders tense? Do your feet point outwards when you land? Do your arms swing across your body as you go along? All of these can hold you up so correct them if you can, though remember there is not one ideal style – even Tulloh sticks his elbows out, Ron Franklin tugs his vest and Andy Ferguson natters away.

Rule no. 6: Be adventurous. Don't be the average runner. In a race his thoughts are set in the play-safe, no-risk mode: 'Well, it's early in the race, better conserve some energy for later . . . . perhaps I should pick up a little now, no, must be careful not to burn out . . . . only a mile to go now . . . . wait for the final 200 metres before showing what I'm really worth . . . . want to do well in the final straight . . . . oops someone's overtaking and I'm too tired to respond . . . . promise to next time . . . . it doesn't matter for now.' Anything for an easy unstressed life you argue. But it *does* matter, because what is to show that you really will do it next time?

Take risks when the unexpected crops up, surge when you're

70

threatened, if you're behind your split schedule inject a fast mile, hang onto the shoulder of your unbeaten rival and decide this is the time to beat him.

Rule no. 7: No pain, no gain. Understand that your threshold of pain is higher than you think. Top racers clear that barrier. They rationalise their pain and run *with* it on the day that matters. The 40-year-old champion, Les Roberts, ex-bicycle racer, in his 5K race at the World Veteran Championships in Rome 1985 finished the final 400m in a scintillating 60sec. The opposition who had been sitting on his shoulder throughout were left floundering. His cycling had taught him to stick in there come what may, for in cycling it is imperative to stay in the slip-stream of the competitor in front, for if you fall back you are lost for good.

Rule no. 8: Boost your ego. The energy and confidence created by a good race or training session is immeasurably greater than that produced by years of dogged no-hope training. So do everything possible to make each training session a success, and organise yourself to work up to a winning race.

There are many tricks. Here are some: Tackle your favourite race distance only sparingly. Do over-distance races and under-distance races in between, more for training. Then have a go again at the special distance. You should do well. The over-distance will have strengthened you and the under-distance given you speed.

In training don't record the same endless times for repetition work. If you have been doing 400s at the same pace all season with a jog recovery, try fewer repetitions or a two-minute break recovery. You should do them better. Then build on that.

If in a session you find you are not maintaining form miss out a repetition so that you come back strongly. It will make you feel a whole lot better than ending up doing several poor efforts.

Rule no. 9: Persistence. Never give up. Had a bad year? It happens to every runner. So make sure you're there for a better one next year. One of the joys of veteran competition is that there's time for comebacks. Every five years you are once more in contention.

It really is a learning process. I heard one new veteran woman at Rome declare that she had learnt more in the races there than in any done previously. There she was watched by many an experienced and knowledgeable runner, who were free with comments, advice and criticism – abrasive but helpful.

Where else but in the veteran movement can you have advice from the best quite free? Thane Baker, triple medallist of the post-war Olympics, gave me personal advice on injury prevention; Peter Higgins, British ex-Olympic 400m medallist, coached me to a medal at his distance despite my having no real earlier training at it. His advice was simply: 'Go out fast and loose and then hang on.' Not bad advice for any racer, really.

9 THE AVALANCHE OF WOMEN

Now is the time for the Year of the Running Woman. However great the benefits of running for men they are so much the greater for women – in improving their looks, their shape, their enjoyment of life, their physical and mental confidence and most especially their health.

Yet it's harder to get the women started!

I decided a while ago that I would do what I could to help, by promoting a campaign to get women on the roads and the tracks.

There had already been signs of a build-up in the past year or two, so a campaign would come at a propitious moment. In 1985 women's running had set a number of records: the high-circulation *Woman's Own* magazine launched its Hyde Park run, a 10k, with 4,000 entries in the first year, making it the biggest ever woman's only event in England; the Strathclyde 10k-OK produced a turn-out of 1,200, a best ever for Scotland; and in Ireland the great Dublin 10ks had grown over some years to a level approaching 10,000 competitors.

Other signs were the publication of Alison Turnbull's book *Running Together* published by George Allen and Unwin and of *Running Magazine*'s special supplement for women.

Among park joggers on the track and at club level I could read the evidence too; at my own club in London, Highgate Harriers, for instance, there was substantial recruitment during the past two years among girls, senior women and veteran women. The British Veterans Athletic Federation reported increasing numbers in the women's events.

What was needed now was to turn this into snowball growth. A nudge here and there and the snowball would be rolling down a thousand different hillsides, knocking over tens of thousands of women and gathering them up in its bulk. I could see a large proportion of veteran women being caught up in that avalanche and I wondered how to use them at the leading edge of the movement.

Coming of age at 35, as women vets do, they have good reason to be leaders and pioneers. They are by that time settled and sensible members of the community, and if family women they have by 40 got the hardest part of their child-bearing under control. (Pregnancy, interestingly, seems to bring out extra strength for running.)

Most important, by their 30s women need to take the threat of heart disease seriously, at least as seriously as losing their shapeliness. For some unaccountable reason the publicity about blood-vessel disease has until now left many women untouched, imagining that they are outside the terms of reference – immune from the epidemic of the age! Yet heart attacks and strokes carry off both sexes in large contingents day after day throughout the year. Professor John Catford of the University of Wales has likened the scale of the fatalities in Britain to those in a jumbo jet crashing every day. Make no mistake, both men and women are booked onto those jumbos.

The message must get through to women that it's just as important for them to avoid the causes of heart disease, including smoking, stress and overweight, and that running is the best way of dealing with these. In my (lay) opinion it is many times more effective than attempts to control the diet; distinguished scientists have made the point. Professor Michael Oliver, a cardiologist, for instance, put forward last year at the British Association for the Advancement of Science his belief that advice on food and cholesterol levels had made little impact on death rate from heart disease – there was no actual proof that eating less high-fat food altered the risk of the disease.

This should be taken seriously in public health quarters, advice should switch to more encouragement of exercise, whose effectiveness has been proven, instead of distracting people with hopes that they can *eat* their way back to health and safety. Women are particularly susceptible to settling for this easy option.

So let's get them running, I said to myself, that's the simplest and best exercise, a positive way of keeping the heart and lungs in condition. It would be my task to nudge away at the snowball, turning on one woman at a time.

I looked around for a first suitable case for treatment, an Over 35 woman who might be converted into running. I didn't have to look far. Donna Dawson, a mother aged 36, was already quite fitness conscious. She was a journalist, which would make her an especially good catch, for she could go out and influence others, and the landslide would get going . . . .

It didn't take much effort to put to her the benefits of running – for a busy working mother it seemed ideal: cheap, quick, friendly and health-giving. She absolutely agreed with me – yet made no attempt to get started. Why? She said she was too pressed for time and confessed she would feel self-conscious about running.

'Just try it once, no one will notice you. You'll soon become a devoted runner,' I begged. 'You'll be hooked.'

She looked at me and said 'Okay, Sylvester, soon as I get time.' Not very convincing! This was the moment for cunning; I'd get at her through her weakest point, I thought, the scent of a good story. So I told her of two very enterprising women runners at Bromley in South London who would be material for an article on how running had benefitted them. Perhaps she would go out for me to discover the secrets of the Running Woman – from the inside. 'Become my mole!'

That appealed to her. Off she went and here tells the story of Nanette and Elizabeth.

Bromley Lady No. 1

Nanette Cross is secretary of the Bromley Ladies Athletic club. Not long ago she was a stone overweight and feeling out of shape after the birth of her two children (Andrew, born 1971 and Louise, born 1974). As a girl she had been active in athletics and hockey but stopped playing when she left school.

Later she resumed hockey, where she met her husband John. But it was viewing the first London Marathon that inspired her; with the memories of the marvels of running from her hurdling days she began training in earnest in October 1981 aged 41.

She never forgot the first training run she did: 'After the first mile I had to stop and walk. Even with all the hockey I wasn't as fit as I thought I was!' But the challenge was important so she steadily worked up to 30 miles a week. She ran her first marathon at Gillingham in 1982. The weather was cold and rainy, with a few hailstones for good measure, and at mile 17 it began to hurt. She wondered if she was in over her head! Despite discomfort she finished in 4:20. A few months later she ran the London Marathon in 3:49. One year later in the Fourth London Marathon, 1984, she knocked 20 minutes off that time. Good progress!

During this period Nanette lost a full stone, purely through running, and now maintains her ideal weight of 9½ stone with no problem. Her stomach has firmed up, as have her thighs and buttocks. She never consciously diets as she finds that running itself acts to stem her appetite: 'I don't pick and nibble like I used to.' It has also made her more aware of what she's eating and when she eats it.

Being a mother there are always problems finding the time to run. When Nanette started she ran in the mornings to fit in with her children's schooling, but now athletics is a large part of family life. Her husband John caught the running bug himself; she had lured him out on one of her training runs. And her children too began to run. Andrew, with his father, joined Blackheath Harriers when he was 11 and Louise joined her mother in Bromley Ladies. Blackheath Harriers and Bromley Ladies train together at Norman Park on Tuesdays, Thursdays and Sundays. At those times she keeps an eye on her children while fulfilling her official capacity as secretary, and does her own training at other times. Twice a week she and a friend run five miles to keep each other motivated on the days that self-motivation is weak: 'I know she's expecting me to join her and I cannot let her down. And it's the same for her.' The rest of her running time is taken up with fartlek training (alternating fast and slow running for speed work), as she is now doing hurdles and sprints. During the winter she enjoys cross-country runs.

At Norman Park she sees women of all ages joining the club to get fit, to lose some weight and to take on the challenge of running several miles. They keep coming because they see and feel the benefits. Nanette has many tips for new runners, such as the importance of a healthy well-balanced diet. She does not bother with low-fat foods as 'Runners need energy from their food with which to run.' Also 'If you only spend money on one thing spend it on well-made, well-fitting running shoes.' To beginners particularly she advises running only *every other day* 'to give the body a chance to recover and readjust,' and to do 20 minutes of stretching exercises to loosen muscles and joints before running fast. 'Even if you don't feel like stretching *make* yourself.'

Nanette has not had much trouble from jeering men but the few that do jeer get invited to 'make a race of it'. Of those who take up the challenge, most drop out and admit defeat; for the few that stick with her, she says 'All right, you've made your point, now leave me alone.' They invariably do. Generally she recommends ignoring them completely.

One of her proudest achievements to date was being part of the Bromley Ladies' Relay Team at the National Veterans Indoor Track Championships at RAF Cosford in March, 1985. They set a new women's vets world record at the time for the 4×100m relay in 59.36 seconds.

Bromley Lady No. 2

Elizabeth Good, the other Bromley lady, aged 52, likes running in the morning. One summer's day in 1978 her husband, Arthur, then 58, asked her to come with him for a run. She was 45 – and she went. She had no special shoes, just a pair of plimsolls. After managing a mile around Crystal Palace Park she remembers feeling really good. In fact so good, she entered the *Sunday Times* Fun Run in Hyde Park that year and managed all two-and-a-half miles of it. She needed reviving with ice lollies at the finish!

The next year, she joined the Crystal Palace Jogging Club (who were instrumental in getting the Jogging Trail established in the Park) and spent Sunday mornings with 30-40 others running, stopping every 15 minutes to do exercises. In this fashion they would manage four miles. Liz was running on her own also and clocked 15 miles a week.

As Arthur was going to run the 1980 People's Marathon in Birmingham Liz decided to enter too. Having done no more than seven miles at any one go, she planned to do only half, but at that point she felt so good she carried on, albeit slowly. At the 20 mile point she popped into a loo and on popping out discovered a man taking down all the direction signs believing everyone had passed! With a bit of coaxing he left the remaining signs up and she trailed in long after the others in just under six hours. Now she really had been bitten by the bug; she has taken part in eight more Marathons since then, improving the time to near four-and-a-half hours. Since they started Liz and Arthur have run in over 140 races together.

In 1984 she joined Bromley Ladies AC to take part in an inter-club 25 mile relay race at Crystal Palace track. She was chosen to do the last lap. She remembers feeling very exposed and alone (all the other runners had finished) but managed it thanks to the shouts of encouragement from members of Blackheath Harriers.

Up until recently her training mileage varied between 25 and 40 miles per week. 'I'd start off aiming at 40,'she says, 'but quite often would slide down to 25.' On Tuesday and Thursday evenings she meets up with fellow club members for a 5 mile run. At the moment there is no clubhouse so they assemble in the car park, have a chat, and set off, different groups running at their different paces. She admits, a bit guiltily, that she gets away without any pre-run stretching but is adamant about owning a pair of good-fitting, well-padded running shoes. (She uses Saucony shoes for training and a pair of Nikes for racing because they are lighter.) She has lost 1½ stone through running and her friends all comment on how well she is looking. In fact she has not been ill for ages and feels much better in herself. If she misses a run for some reason she feels bad about it all day: 'I know I feel better when I've done it!' Her advice to other women who have been indecisive about running is: 'Just get out there and do it.'

Donna handed me these profiles of the Bromley ladies adding, 'Wait though, I've something else to come that's really special. Two Supervet women of Over 60 – I'm off to interview them next week.'

'Oh yes?' said I.

'Neither *started* running until they were well over 60. That'll dispel the myth that you can be too old to start. Neither has come to any grief – in fact their health and well-being have positively bloomed and they've made new friendships. I'm going to run with one of them!' Donna went on enthusiastically, 'Tell you what: how

78

about it if I interview her jogging alongside?'

'Why not,' I agreed, trying to be rather cool about it, 'why not indeed?' To myself I chortled: 'So Donna's jogging, is she?'

Over 60 Lady No. 1

For forty-two years Peggy Taylor had been a spectator at her husband Bill's racing and for forty-two years he had always said 'Are you coming?' when he went out for a run. She had always said 'No' – until, in October 1984, at the age of 65, she found herself saying 'Wait for me!'

Her discontent at being merely a spectator had been growing for years. At the European Veterans Championships in Brighton, 1984, Peggy was moved at the end of the ceremony when the German veterans spontaneously picked up a Union Jack and ran around the stadium to show their appreciation of British hospitality. At that moment, she felt part of an international brotherhood – and sisterhood – of runners. The last spur was reading the 'Getting Started' chapter in *The AAA Runner's Guide* which 'made good sense' to her. She bought herself a comfortable pair of running shoes and was waiting ready to say 'Yes' to Bill the next time he asked.

Bill was wise enough to curb her beginner's enthusiasm by insisting that she start off with long walks. After a month of this she graduated to jogging between lampposts only, up to a distance of three miles. He also told her she could only run every other day – poor Peggy was chafing at the bit! Before her training had even started Bill suggested she lose some weight first, because her blood pressure was creeping up: she managed to take off half a stone through watching her diet and using an exercise bike. Once she had actually started running, she worked out a routine for herself that she looked forward to: up at 7.30am, 20 minutes of warm-up, feed the cats and make a drink, and out of the door at 8.15 for a 45-minute run. Both she and Bill run around a wood near their Oxfordshire home, often together. Bill soon strikes out in another direction, but doubles back to check up on her (Bill has been running since he was 10, and joined the March Athletics Club in 1976. His specialities are the 800m and 1500m; he captured a European Gold in the over-60s 800m in 1978, as well as a bronze in the same event in the 1979 Veteran World Championships).

As a schoolgirl Peggy had never liked the kind of running they were forced to do, which consisted of 'belting around the field as fast as you could go.' It gave her a stitch. Until she met Bill she had learned to hate running. She had maintained an active lifestyle, however, with plenty of walking and swimming. When she started running, she was worried about injury to her ankles, always a weak spot for her. But due to choosing good shoes and starting off slowly, she's had no problems at all – not even a blister!

In May 1985 she ran her first vets race at Cannock in the Midlands: it was the 100m, in a time of 20.8sec. The world standard for the over 65s is 20 seconds! After running in a wood she found it strange to be running in lanes. On June 9th she ran the 100m at the Barnet Sports Gala in 20.6, and later that month she ran the 100m in 20.4, and the 200m in 44.8, at the Bucks, Berks, Oxon and Hants Championship. She followed this with a run of 19.79 – below the 20 at last – at the Vets International in Baden, Switzerland, in July. She was improving all the time. Up to the end of July 1985, she had competed in no fewer than six veteran events.

Peggy noticed that running helped her breathing and also decreased her appetite. She finds that instead of stuffing herself, she actually eats less rather than more. Her diet is a healthy one: muesli in the morning, bread and cheese for lunch, and maybe fish with two vegetables for dinner. 'It's boredom that makes you eat,' she says. She doesn't believe that running has helped her lose weight – she attributes that more to diet – but according to Peggy 'it's put everything back in its right place!' She runs every day, even in winter, but gives it a miss if it's icy. Her advice to older beginners is not to forget that vital 20-minute warm-up before going out (she particularly recommends yoga for suppleness, and has practised it for years), to dress warmly in cold weather and a 20-minute warm-down period to keep joints and muscles from seizing up. She thinks running in a town might make her nervous, but suggests a running partner for anyone who is. 'Running is something that *anyone* can do,' she says, 'just doing it gets you hooked!'

Over 60 Lady No. 2

When Jenny Wood Allen ran her first marathon in Dundee in April 1983, she was 71 years old. She had been a council worker for eleven years, serving both on the District Sports Council and the Committee for Sport for the Disabled. The Sports Council were looking for people to sponsor in this very marathon and Jenny thought 'What about me?' No one in the sporting world would touch her when she made her thoughts known, but she passed the university fitness tests (heart, lungs, blood pressure), with no problems. After all she had been a competitive cyclist in earlier years, winning the 15-mile Dundee trophy two years in succession in the early 1930s – but seventeen years had elapsed between the last cycling and her first stab at running. Nonetheless, she started her training in an ordinary pair of flat shoes and no running gear, choosing quiet places where no one would see her. She knew she would have to lose some weight before the race and by sticking to a high-fibre vegetarian diet she gradually got down to 9st 7lb from 10st 2lb. She's 5ft 4in.

The physiotherapist of Dundee football club called her a 'very determined woman indeed' and promised to treat any injuries incurred while training for the marathon. She did have knee trouble to start with, but this was due to the wrong kind of running shoe. For Christmas she was given a pair of the right kind!

Her family thought 'Mother's going mad', but when they saw her determination they all rallied round to support her. In fact, when she ran that first marathon in 5:34 her sons and grand-children ran sections of it with her, while her disabled husband cheered from the sidelines.

Now she runs the Dundee and Glasgow marathons every year with some half marathons in-between. Her time for the 1985 Dundee marathon of 4:21 was then a new world record for her age-group, despite rain, snow and hail!

Jenny trains five to six days a week including runs of 5, 8 or 10 miles with a 15 miler at the weekend. She has spent only three weeks off running when she fell over a curb on a long-distance run and dislocated her shoulder. She soon recovered.

In the summer of 1985 Jenny found a companion for one run a week and now enjoys it still more. It also helps her speed because they can pace each other. Running has given her new-found strength and suppleness: 'Before I started running, I could hardly raise my feet high enough to get over broken ground; now I can lift my foot onto the table and get my head down to my knee.' She covers her training mileage in the early mornings or at lunchtime, and twice a week she goes to the running track in Caird Park, Dundee, to do fartlek training, 2 laps as fast as possible, then 1 lap at a slow jog for recovery, 2 more fast laps, and so on, up to half an hour. The coach times her on a 3 or 6-mile run, and gives her training charts to follow. Twice a week she visits a multi-gym and spends 45 minutes there.

Her motivation to get out there and run is that she feels she must keep her fitness up in order to compete in the marathons. Her advice to older women who are just starting off is to have a fitness test first, and like Peggy to do a good 20-minute warm-up before going out (this is more important the older you are). Also, Jenny advises a 'cool down' period to get your heartbeat back to normal. She follows a schedule of exercises for this: neckrolls, arm and leg stretching, lunges, and so on. She maintains that you don't need any special running gear – just a pair of good shoes. 'Start off slowly .to build up stamina,' she says; '*then* cultivate speed. Running is a first-class way of exercising, and a very handy one – you just go out your front door and start.'

Peggy and Jenny are careful to warm up (as well as stretch). This is particularly important for post-menopausal women who some-times suffer from more stress fractures because of the reduction of oestrogen in their bodies; exercise may help to keep such fractures at bay through maintaining the bone mineral content. Oestrogen replacement therapy is the surest way to avoid brittle bones, and the problems that come with them, though the pros and cons of such therapy must be discussed with your doctor.

'So those are the stories,' said Donna.

'And now let's come to Donna's story,' said I, 'and I think I know the ending!'

'Donna's story?' she asked.

'What about those interviews while jogging for instance?'

'Oh, yes,' she said, 'I see what you mean. Well, doing these profiles led to many hours of interviewing women runners and reading about the benefits of running, and the longer I sat in my chair and wrote, the more my back ached and my feet itched. I was constantly receiving reinforcement on views I tentatively held: that running firmed up the flabby bits, made you less prone to illness, gave you a healthy glow, cleared your mind, improved your cardiovascular system, gave you more energy, helped control your weight and generally made you more aware of a healthier lifestyle.

'I was also being made aware of what it didn't do: it didn't hurt a woman's reproductive cycle (in fact, it brought about less painful periods), make her breasts droop (they firm up!), or damage her unborn baby (women who become pregnant *can* run – albeit carefully and if they are used to it, and have no medical reason why not – with no harm coming to the foetus).

'After I had Emily, three years ago at the age of 33, I noticed that the old body just wasn't bouncing back into shape as quickly as I would have liked it to, despite long forays into keep-fit. I thought of running, which is easy to do when you live as close to Crystal Palace park and the built-in jogging trail as I do, and the sight of runners pounding round the park as I wheeled Emily in her push-chair was a constant reminder of what I could do if I could only get organised. My problem was *time*: after a full day's work, I would rush home to pick up Emily from nursery/childminder/husband, while said husband went out to his trumpet-playing job in the West End. If I went out at *all*, it would have to be early mornings or weekends – and I had convinced myself that I wasn't an early morning person! Also I felt rather self-conscious about it all.

'Well, while doing my interviews, noting these other women's experiences, I decided to give it a try. One morning I made the effort. I was up early and donning my High Tech shoes and tracksuit, I went for a run. The first few minutes were the worst, as I struggled to get my breathing in rhythm with my body, but once the rhythm was established, my mind cleared and emptied and my body took over. I noticed how bright the morning sunshine was (when else would you see it?!), and when I spotted another two runners, I said 'Hello.' They said 'Hello' back – like we were all in this together! For the rest of the day, I felt full of energy – lungs clear and open and I even managed to get rid of some troublesome phlegm that was bothering me. I ran on the next two days as well, and promptly pulled a leg muscle even though I'd warmed up for ten minutes beforehand! I had learned Lesson Number One: When you first start, run only every other day for at least a month until your body adjusts. Otherwise, it doesn't get enough time to recover. One other thing I learned: I *can* run in the mornings, after all.'

'And do you know something, a little secret, I do believe I might be hooked myself . . . . '

I smiled and said nothing though inside I felt rather smug.

'And I'm thinking of joining Bromley Ladies.'

'Why not, Donna. Why not indeed!' said I. A very nice ending to Donna's story.

★   ★   ★

So that was one more woman on the run! But one swallow doesn't make a movement. More were needed, many many more. I knew that Donna herself would pass the message on – each one teach one – but I had to find other ways of influencing women, in batches, nay battalions! The logical step would be to get them running at my own club first.

But, too late, because the movement was already under way there, I'm pleased to report, just beginning, but it was to turn out a great success. This is the story of that success, of how the women themselves brought it about, a model of organisation and determination. Here is an example to be followed by clubs and groups in all parts of Britain. One club can set another going and that one can start two more rolling and they can all outdo each other until the whole island is jumping up and down with the thundering feet of the tribe of women.

It was Sarah Cawkwell who started things going at my club, Highgate Harriers, famous for its long slow distance group, which for years has attracted hundreds of runners over its 10 mile trail at 9am on Sundays. From time to time novice women had turned up for this run, but many could not stay the pace and dropped out dispirited. Sarah, herself a vet, realised sadly that women were being frightened off for good by this unpleasant experience. It was a sorry situation. The main loss was not to the group but to the women themselves, for they would never realise the endless benefits that running brings – benefits, to reiterate, that in the end are greater for women than for men, because women have greater amounts of confidence and courage to find than men, confidence to realise that there is more to life than the media projection of women, and courage to be able to get out and run in the first place. Being in the world of running supplies both these. There are also benefits of especial interest to women such as improved circulation, which makes a person less prone to *feeling* cold. Varicose veins, primarily a women's complaint, can be helped if not prevented, by better circulation.

The menstrual cycle is often less stressful – it could be argued that men benefit indirectly from that one!

So Sarah decided to create a sheltered environment for her women, to help to coax them into regular running. She needed a small class of recruits to start with. She used the high moment of the 1985 London Marathon to recruit them, by advertising on notice boards in libraries, education centres and sports shops and in London's event magazines. Soon she began receiving telephone calls. She assembled her group at the 9 o'clock start-point, but made sure that they were not pressurised by the superfit regulars, and set them off separately on a relaxed and slow 3 miler. There were differences of ability even in this novice group, so she split them further into slow and slow-slow sections, and one very slow-slow-slow overweight mum. The group hardly grew at first, as many dropped out in spite of the gentle handling, and reinforcements were needed. They came through a listing of beginners' groups by *Woman's Own*, until by the end of four months 30 or 40 had turned out, many of them veterans, some as once-onlies, but most as members of a circle of regulars. These regulars progressed to circuits of 6 and even 10 miles, meeting often during the week for a companionable run. Many then joined Highgate Harriers and went on to greater things although of course absolute beginners were still given top attention, even walked back round the course if their second wind did not materialise. The group developed something of a social spirit and began to take over the running of its affairs.

I ran with this Slow-and-Easy-group once or twice to meet some of the regulars: One was Sue Reynolds, aged 36, a mother of two boys who themselves became club runners, as did her husband

Bob. Sport for all! Both Sue and Bob have now given up smoking, are experiencing a striking change in their shapes and looks, and feeling their youth return. A classic metamorphosis. Could anything like that be done on low-fat diets or transcendental meditation? Of the rest of the group virtually every woman did the *Woman's Own* 10K, and went on to further competition.

This was the result of just one woman's part-time effort – multiply it around the country, I thought, and you really could mobilise a mass movement. So that's a pattern for veteran women all over Britain: get a small, slow group going inside each of your clubs.

Here's some advice for those starting such a group. First of all it is easier to share the work with a partner: between you you can cover holidays and so on. Then be patient and persevering, especially at the beginning; many beginners will fall away so that you could even find yourself one week with no class at all. You need to build up a core of enthusiasts, slowly, slowly . . . . with new input continuing through the year, until you have arrived at critical mass!

Take the names and addresses of all who contact you, so that you can send them reminders if they seem to be backsliding. Treat the new ones very tenderly until they build up confidence and rise to find their natural level of ability. (That's another reason to have a partner, so that there are enough of you to officer two or three subgroups at different speeds.) Encourage the women to take an active part in the organisation of their club – help *them* to help *you*.

In due course, to stimulate them further, enter the group for a fun run or even a hard race. Nothing brings out the best in a new runner so much as a bit of competition.

That will be your final reward, leading a dozen or more of your own recruits to the tape, even being headed by one who might become a champion.

10 SUPERVETS – THE OVER 60s

When you turn 60 you move into an entirely new classification, the Supervets. You become a world leader, showing the way to a time when all remain full of vigour until 100 years of age, instead of slumping into lumpish retirement.

The next target? The Over 100s, the Super Methuselahs? Who doubts that by the start of the Third Millenium medical science will have us all patched up for this super age-group, artificial hearts, hips and kidneys to order, replanted teeth, thick new heads of hair, and noses remoulded to the height of fashion?

It is up to us to maintain the youthful spirit to go with all this. An input of zestful running will see to that as well as to muscle condition. Recent research has shown that the longer and harder the brain is used the more of its capacity and power is retained. They've shown it in rats; they've shown it in some ordinary citizens too. I like to think it's simply the training effect again – exercise freshening up the blood supply to the brain, which is enabled to strengthen and regenerate itself to prepare for the next demand on it.

Living on and on will only be worthwhile if we are blessed with full bodily health and mental alertness. That is certainly the state of any Supervet runner: high performance, heightened awareness and the highest motivation. You can observe the Supervets everywhere, when running or racing – they don't have that spiritless, resigned look on the face.

There never was for instance such a bright and positively cheeky character as Duncan Maclean, the 'Tartan Flash', even at the age of 93, which was when last I saw him.

Full of repartee and reminiscence – his memory stretched back not only to his youth before the turn of the century, but was also accurate and perceptive about events of the recent past – he was always eager to see a friend.

He did a little skip into the air and a rush along the corridor to greet me on that final occasion. Was it the fact that he finally retired from running on medical advice that led to his death within the year?

In this superhuman attempt to improve the species and the length of its lifespan, once again veteran runners are pioneers. No wonder – they want to enjoy the world longer. They want to extract the full fun of competition in their racing no matter what their age. Why should spoilt youth be entitled to a monopoly of the blessings? It's time the opportunities were made available to all. Join the revolution!

The racing arrangements in veteran athletics nurture this attempt to keep motivation going. As a result runners in their late 50s positively look forward to their 60th birthdays, as they emerge from being oldest in the 55-59 age-group to becoming the youngest and spryest in the next – an extra edge to the spirit of competition! At major race events the organisers are heedful to fit in races in five-year age divisions going right up the scale.

Once the 60s and 70s were at the leading edge of the racing boom; today at big championships there are not only specific sections for the Over 80s, but even for the Over 85s and Over 90s, though only two or three individuals may have entered at this incredible level.

Few have ever been as well-placed as I was when entering the Over 60 category. My 60th birthday, long awaited, was on December 25th, 1980, while the start of the World Veterans Championships, which was the effective date for age reckoning, was two weeks later, January 7th. I was as new-born a Supervet as could be, at last sheltered from the threatened presence of the fiendishly fast Dick Stolpe, the Yank who had been 55 when I was 59½ and able to leave me yards behind. (Be assured that a four or five-year differential is all the difference in the world, a big handicap to the older man, costing me more than a second for example in my specialist event, the 200m. However limber you remain, year by year, inexorably, your speed drops away by a fraction. I had run 25.3 when I was 55, I would surely slow to the 26.5 four years later.)

Our plane touched down in New Zealand, where the week-long championships were to be held, on the very day of my birthday, and we were seen into the airport buildings at Auckland by grumpy airline staff – mad no doubt at having to work on that day of the year, on my birthday! We travelled down from the North Island to the South on a slow holiday tour, with opportunity to train on the sands all the way, from Simpson's Camp and Manganui to Wellington and Christchurch, where were gathered two thousand runners from the countries of the world. That's one of the great enjoyments of being in the veteran scene: every two years there is a world championship and in the between years there is a European championship, so there is somewhere new and friendly to holiday every year. You enter at your own request on very low qualifying standards, and you pay your own way.

In New Zealand in 1981 in the 200m at age 60 I won the gold in 26.81sec – that compares with the 25.1 I recorded for my silver medal behind Dick Stolpe (then 54, he 50,) at the first world games in Toronto in 1975. So generally I was slowing down by one per cent or so a year, quite the normal rate.

Beginners of 60

Turning Supervet is as much an occasion as a 21st birthday. How much more honour to those Supervets who only enter the running movement after 60. Thousands of them have done just this, not a few even older, well into their 70s. Some have gone on to become famous performers.

In the Over 60s sprints, my own category, three men arrived from nowhere these past few years to take part in serious competition. One would think they'd been lurking all their lives, waiting until 60 to spring out and challenge those of us regular members of the vet circus of track performers.

We old stagers weren't resentful of them barging in then to take some of the honours from us; on the contrary we welcomed them, because in Britain until then there was only rather softer competition at our level. We needed some stretching out.

First Alan Lovett turned up, a cheery all-rounder from Surrey; then came a famous Rugby international of the 1940s, Les Williams from Wales, who'd kept very fit coaching over the years; and then a retired headmaster from Rochdale in Lancashire, Alan

Bowdler. (Of course retirement can often be the signal to make your debut.)

At their first appearance those of us already competing in their age class were treated with much respect. 'I've had such inspiration hearing about you fellows,' Les Williams flattered us. In a lordly way we gave them a bit of informal coaching and advice. A year later to our surprise we found that they were right on our heels, and in the third year they overtook us, both Williams and Bowdler winning national titles off us. It was an important moment for them and also for the rest of us, because it obliged us to produce more effort and motivation all round, instead of reclining on our laurels. I myself was caused to dig into my sprint training very seriously once again and in due course improved enough to hold them off in some of the major fixtures. 'We've had such inspiration from you,' I joshed.

The experiences of these three also demonstrates a heartening principle that you can rely on. If you come to running as a veteran, whether you were a crack runner at an earlier stage of your life, or not, you will be able to count on fully three or four years of continuing improvement before you reach your peak. You learn the technique, your muscles pick up a great deal from the training you subject them to, and you harness new motivation.

When I started my vet career, aged 51, I could only manage 33.1secs for the 200m. The following year I worked hard and consistently – my time dipped below 28 seconds. Then in 1974 I began to reckon out just how to explode out of the blocks, fly around the bend and hold my form coming up the straight. I notched up a number of wins in the 26 second range.

At last in 1975, aged 54, I reached my life-time peak – 24.8secs. After that began the slow, regular and inevitable one per cent per year slide. Nevertheless, in 1985, aged 64, I was still able to run a 27.1 second 200m, three seconds faster than I could manage when I first took up competitive running thirteen years previously.

Speeding up in the Marathon

So it's possible to keep getting faster as you grow older. Among distance runners it seems quite the normal thing – age is less of a handicap for them anyway. A startling marathoning example in Britain in the 1980s was that of Laurie Forster of Hemel Hempstead, a man not far off the Supervets class. This one-time cyclist showed up in a few races in the South – marathons and 10 miles – a rather deferential figure, very willing to learn from the old hands, some of whom had never been away from the race circuits in 40 or 50 years of athletics. But soon Laurie began to win local races, then regional events and within a few months tackled the London Marathon. This was 1983 and he recorded 2:59. Getting under the three hour mark was far too tempting. 'I knew then that something was "on"', Laurie told me while we were travelling back from a race together last autumn.

Something was certainly 'on'. The following year – he keeps his marathon efforts to only one or two a year – he did 2:48. His latest 'London', 1985, was a 2:34:32, sensational on two or three years experience: it was an Over 55 British record. He also improved to personal bests in 1985 at his other distances, 10,000m, 5,000m and the Indoors 1,500m. In the World Games in Rome 1985 he came fourth in the 5,000m, this tyro runner. I predict that he will continue to improve his time and is a certainty for a medal in the 1987 World Games at Melbourne.

Laurie Forster was another classic case of the man in his 50s, heavy smoker, overweight and drifting through life – on his own admission – who hesitantly took up running as a cure, never having run before and with not the slightest knowledge that he had an exceptional talent for it.

The running cognoscenti have now spotted another marathoner ready to go for a record or two as he speeds up through his apprenticeship years. This is Frank Dobson, another southerner, another cyclist-turned-marathoner, just into his early 60s.

When he first showed up at the Mitcham 25K, an historic event, organised by Jack Fitzgerald, a famous veteran runner, who manages things so efficiently that he is able to run it as well as run *in* it, he created quite a furore. Unknown at 60, he threatened not only Jack, a noted Over 60 performer, but other latter-day stars. By 1985, his second year of competition, Dobson took second place in two top competitions and was quite expected to go on to challenge for the national championship in 1986. Learn as you go!

Flying Scots

Jenny Wood Allen of Dundee, aged 71 when she began running (see Chapter 9) is of course another case of a runner improving steadily during her first years. 'If only the process could go on indefinitely,' says Jenny wistfully. Perhaps, with the advance hand in hand of medical science and athletic training procedures, it will at least be possible for us to avoid going slower as we get older . . . . to be in a world where there is no downhill!

These Scots seem to have specialised in producing Supervets over the past few years. Both the Over 60 and Over 70 British marathon titles are held by men from Scotland, Hugh Currie of Glasgow in the younger category and Gordon Porteous in the senior. There's John Farrell too, a 75-year-old Scot, who was champion of his class at the World Veterans 10K at Lytham St Annes in 1985.

Hugh Currie is another of those Johnny-come-latelies. When he won the London Marathon Over 60 title in April, 1985, the other veterans in that group, all well-known themselves, as well as being knowledgeable about others in the field, looked very sceptically at Currie's name on the results list. How could someone have gatecrashed from nowhere straight into the medals? 'Must be a younger bloke using a contraband entry ticket,' they shrugged.

What they meant was that in the strictly rationed London Marathon someone had worked a black market racket: a strong young runner, easily capable of the 2:48 attributed to Currie in the results, had bought the number from the unknown older vet and run under his colours.

But the innocent and impressive truth began to emerge. At the next big distance event, the world veteran 25K at Lytham St Annes, while they were grunting up the hills, alongside each other, two or three of the Over 60s discovered in conversation that there was indeed an up and coming Scott veteran named Currie; finally his story and achievements were dug out by a friend and given a publicity airing, Hugh Currie himself being a rather modest man. I heard the story from his friend and fellow runner, a colleague on the Scottish *Daily Record* and *Sunday Mail*, Jack Newbigging: 'Even in a brotherhood like the vets,' Newbigging wrote me in the summer of 1985, 'one section of the running world doesn't know all the others. I write as past president of the Scottish vets and for 25 years, a friend and colleague of Hugh Currie, the 62-year-old who ran this year's London in 2:48. Hugh was born on 5th March, 1923, and has always been a keen mountaineer and hill-walker. He used to enjoy a few miles' running twice a week, and when he was 50 also took up skiing.

'When we met in 1960, Hugh was a reporter with the *Daily Record*. Now he's the senior editorial manager of the *Daily Record* and *Sunday Mail*. It wasn't till 1978 that Hugh began to run more often, going out almost daily from the office to escape business lunches.'

'His first race was the Scottish Vets half-marathon at Inchinnan, in October, 1980. When he ran 1:27, the Scottish vets newsletter rightly forecast great deeds ahead.

'The very next month Hugh made his marathon debut. It was in the 1980 Barnsley, and I believe a check would show that his 3:09 was top of the Over 55 class. His name wasn't known, though, and the honour went elsewhere. Barnsley was followed by a 3:03 in the 1981 London, a reduction to 2:59 in the Tyneside Marathon then 2:52 in the 1982 Glasgow.

With his 60th birthday coming up in March 1983, Hugh really looked set for a crack at some records. But – isn't there always a but? he dropped out of a local cross-country in November 1982, then began almost two years of knee trouble, till an operation to remove a cyst in late summer 1984.

'Despite the knee, though, and on absolutely zero training – (Apart from running from registration to the start) – he did the 1983 Paris marathon in 3:05. He finished sick and in pain. And first Over 60.

'London 1985 was Hugh's comeback after injury. His 2:48 surprised a few folk who didn't know the man or his history. But a 2:45 wouldn't have surprised his training companions.

'A wiry 5ft 9in 9st 8lb, Hugh is as tough as they come, cheery with it, and still improving! It's too soon to say that John Gilmour's world record 2:39 is beyond him, though he runs for fun and satisfaction, not records.

'His only club is the Scottish Veteran Harriers. Training is about 60 miles a week, and one of Hugh's faults is that he doesn't know what an easy run is.'

The Australian, John Gilmour, is now breaking records in the Over 65 class so won't be too full of compliments if Hugh Currie does annex one of his earlier marks.

Gordon Porteous, the 1985 Over 70 marathon champion of Britain, is another Glaswegian, but with a most contrasting career in running. His marathon career spans 40 years. He first appeared in the Polytechnic race, from Windsor to London, where at the age of 31 and already a successful cross-country runner, he did 3:00:14. By 1985 he had slowed down by a mere ten minutes, clocking 3:11 at the London Marathon!

It's true that during his time he did get as fast as 2:49, at the age of 51, in the Scottish National Championships. However, just cast a look over that curve of his achievements: first a quite workman-like time as a youngish man, then as a 51-year-old, almost a generation on, the same individual outstrips himself: and finally he holds on to his speed indomitably, to give a wavy-looking curve, and with only small fluctuations in performance during a forty-year spell. Porteous has been rewarded for these efforts by boxfulls of trophies won at some time or another, young man and veteran, in marathons, cross-countries and track races.

His latest outstanding performance was the World Over 70 cross-country silver medal at Rome, in 1985.

Porteous believes his training schedule of 50 miles a week has been the key to his success.

I followed another very successful marathon runner's career right from its beginning. This man, Stephen Richardson, was a family friend long before he took to racing, when a champion at quite another sport, dinghy racing. Stephen in these days used to be very intrigued about my running career. It turned out that he had as a friend and neighbour Jim Fixx, the writer: actually it was through Jim's, not my influence, that he took to running, and got so very far.

Stephen, a professor of sociology, is an American but he was originally English, a cousin of the great actor, Sir Ralph Richardson, in fact. During the war Stephen was in the merchant navy. Soon after VE day he jumped ship in New York, settled in the USA and put himself through a course of higher education.

In his late 50s he began slow running with Fixx in their home patch of Connecticut and found that it quite suited his style. Then, a lanky, bearded figure, he began to show up on the American championship circuit, and before long he was ending races as a winner, sometimes ahead of tried and tested champions. It was the same story – in due course this absolute beginner became the best in the world. He had it in him all the time yet hadn't the slightest idea of his talent. He won the Over 60 title in the New York Marathon and finally at the world Veteran Games in Puerto Rico, 1983, he took the 10,000m gold medal, the Cross-Country gold and the 5,000m bronze. That cross-country! It was held out in the Puerto Rico bush, flat and baking. It was so hot, even the crickets were jumping. By the half-way athletes were folding up in platoons from heat exhaustion. Thirty-two of the field of 250 had to be rushed by helicopter to hospital.

At the next world games cycle, Rome, 1985, Stephen was entered but cancelled at the last minute. The reason? His 65th birthday would be precisely one day after the championships were due to open, which meant that under the rules he would have still been classed as an Over 60, and would be the very oldest man in the category. The luck of the draw but too daunting.

There is a very famous American indeed who takes part in Supervet championships, Senator Alan Cranston, who was a strong contender in 1984 for a different event: Democratic nomination in the Presidential campaign. I have run against him myself – not for Senate, but for the 200m Over 60 title . . . . this was in San Diego a few years back.

We were both beaten by a man who was equally well known in America, as a one-time member of the US Olympic team. This was Payton Jordan, today still setting world records, year by year, as he goes up the age range.

The veteran running movement is spreading up the age range after him, and among women, too. Women supervets have been inspired lately by the efforts of such as Jenny Wood Allen and, in 1985, 71-year-old Carla Ali, who made her marathon debut in the London. It's very impressive to see the fine shape these late, late heroines have got themselves into – novices who had sat out the whole of their three score years and ten as mere spectators.

Is there any reason why women should not grasp the chance, at any age and any stage, to benefit from the personal renaissance that running brings? For women it has the additional advantage that it is superb beauty treatment, it can't help but improve the look of the legs and slim down the waist, useful values for anyone.

Training

In the Supervets life your attention should turn to training schedules especially cut down for the older runner. Don't do this because you may have been frightened by an over-cautious medical adviser, but as a positive way of maximising performance. Over-training will not harm you, I believe, but it will lose you races. Rethink your whole training plan, simply because you won't have the staying power that you had in your prime, and you can't afford to do without a full period of recovery if you are to give of your best.

There are a few who can reckon themselves exceptions to this rule, world-beaters like John Gilmour, still able to turn out an effortless 60 or 70 miles a week in training. But that load-rate of mileage would actually serve to impair an ordinary 65-year-old's performance. So at that age throw in a day's complete rest and a couple of days on an easy jog routine. That gives a better base for racing. More attention could be devoted to concentration, thinking deep into your muscles and your breathing apparatus while out on the road, the kind of concentration some younger people can't easily summon up. Make the most of the advantages of maturity.

If you're doing interval running, undertake fewer repetitions rather than cut down the pace and pattern of the intervals. If you're on hillwork the same applies. When on a fartlek session do the same burst at speed, but take a longer jog recovery between.

The whole of your schedules should be treated pro rata; if you were able to race 10 miles under the hour previously, on a 60–70 mile training load, but you now have slowed to 65 minutes for the distance, perhaps you'll see some logic in a proportional cutting down of the weekly work – your times show that your recovery is not up to what it was and it needs to be given a full spell to be effective. Don't get into a desperate state in trying to hold on to a routine you used to be able to handle happily.

By 60 you should have mastered impatience and youthful folly.

Sylvester and Helper
The trophy storage problem solved by the use
of a wooden medal-man.

PHOTO DOUG POOLE ©

Veteran of the 1980s At the age of 47 Tecwyn (Taff) Davies won his fifth British Over 40 cross-country title and won the world Over 40 10 km road championships.

PHOTO: FRED POPPLEWELL

PHOTO: TERRY RICE, KETTERING

Dollar earner Priscilla Welch who took up running at 34, competed in the British Olympic marathon team at the age of 39 (2:28.54), then spent two years in the U.S. winning substantial road running money prizes against all comers.

LES Runners Joyce Smith, Britain's greatest veteran
woman, still running at world class in her late 40s.
Donna Dawson, aged 36 who took up running in the cause
of research. The Highgate Harriers ladies' distance group.
(Sarah Cawkwell far right)

PHOTO: BRIAN MOODY

PHOTO: LEONE FARRIS

PHOTO: CERI BREEZE

PHOTO: RAY ASPINALL

PHOTO: SARAH HUTCHINGS

LES Runners Leslie Williams, Over 60 British sprint and pentathlon champion. Les Roberts, Rome World Games 5K champion. Les Brown: Over 60 world ranked runner at a range of distances from 200m to 10k. Leslie Watson: Has competed in more than 130 marathons, and won many of them.

Two Generations Bruce Tulloh, famous barefoot
running champion of the 1960s, with his twin daughters
Jojo and Katherine, English cross-country champions.

GB, 1,2,3 Britain's clean sweep in the 1984 European
Championships, Women Over 35. Judy Vernon,
Margaret Williams (formerly Critchley), 1st, and
Janet Roscoe, all of whom competed in the British
Olympic team in 1972.

The Veterans' AC Four former club presidents:
Dave Dellar, Mike McDowell, Peter Harvey, Charlie
Williams.

Guy Ogden, British Over 40 Champion in 1984.
Bridget Cushen. Leading cross-country runner
and member of the International Veterans Committee.

PHOTO: FRED POPPLEWELL

Back from the Brink Four great runners all racing under handicap. John Disley, British Olympic medallist, who has had a hip replaced (here seen measuring race course). John Atkinson, of Barnet AC, runs with a pacemaker in his heart.

PHOTO: MEGGS & SMITH PHOTOGRAPHY

Peter McGhie, who came back to health and
running from a critical lung cancer condition.
Fritz Assmy, World record Over 65 sprinter,
who has been blind since 1938.

PHOTO: FRED POPPLEWELL

Three men who supplied me with inspiration
Peter Halstead as fitness coach and Jack Fitzgerald
as founder figure of the veteran movement.

Al Rockall (112), as running trainer.

PHOTO: JIM SHEARER, DUNDEE

PHOTO: TIMES NEWSPAPERS LTD.

PHOTO: NOEL MANEFFI PHOTOGRAPHY

Supervets Over 60s runners. Jenny Wood Allen,
Sid McSweeney, Peter King, Colin Fairey,
Stephen Richardson, Bryn Jenkins.

PHOTO: *NORTHAMPTONSHIRE*

On the track Two Over 45 runners who have been lifelong competitors, Mike Turner (now 64) and Don McGregor, who was a British Olympic runner in 1972.

You should, for instance, have learned the importance of budgeting more time for recovering from injuries. You'll be making a mistake to hurry back from injury: in the end it'll mean a longer lay-off than in allowing the damaged part to heal fully. Who hasn't known runners who attempt races when not fully repaired and who then find that the rest of the season must be considered a write-off? Who hasn't been such a one!

Patience! It's forced on the veteran, simply because it takes longer for the older athlete's muscle and tendons to regenerate. To keep the tendons easy and flexible is difficult enough for ordinary elderly persons who put no pressure on their musculature – does not every picture tell a story!

When the tendons have become torn or damaged through training or racing they are not only painful in hard action they also stiffen up and thus effectively limit the extension of the injured leg, reducing the stride length. You run a lesser distance in a given time, i.e., you are slower.

Then it becomes necessary to regenerate the tendon, through gentle daily stretching exercises and through the application of alternate hot and cold splashes to the spot, which has the function of stimulating the blood to flow into and out of the hardened tendon until it gradually fills out again, and becomes more pliable and stronger. The affected tissue gains new growth; you have a reconditioned part, good for a further ten thousand miles – if not actually guaranteed.

Through protection and preparation the wisest veterans limit the number of occasions on which they get injured and thus the time of lay-offs. As a result there are thousands of Supervets running on and on with ease. There are illustrious ex-Olympic champions in their 70s and 80s and there are others who have never won a medal, then or now, but run for pleasure. And there is still room for tens of thousands more, so if you are 60 or even well past it, don't think it's too late to start. Get going now, don't put it off for another decade! Perhaps, to your own amazement, you'll end up winning medals.

11 INSULTS TO THE INJURED

No sooner was the great running boom born than a vociferous anti-running lobby came into being. As if responding to Newton's Law, reactionary cliques immediately arose to shout down the benefits that running brings.

They were rushing in to protect their own vested positions, you can be sure. There were the public house philosophers envious of others going out to do themselves some good . . . . the old-fashioned medics genuinely perturbed lest their middle-aged patients should be committing hara-kiri on the hoof, and then resentful at having to repair their sore knees and self-inflicted blisters . . . . the cigarette smoking pressure groups . . . . the newspapers, always ready to play devil's advocate and get a nice caring controversy going . . . . and many others.

Their major ammunition was the 'shocking' number of injuries endured by runners. Their statements caused us keep-fit hopefuls to wonder if they were more concerned about damage to ankles and knees than to hearts and lungs.

The public were quite frightened by the thought of all this injury that awaited them. They imagined runners clogging hospital wards, legs suspended from pulleys, or stumping along, limbs in plaster, like a set of tyro skiers . . . . perhaps even enduring amputations! But in fact runners' injuries are sore calf muscles or strained Achilles tendons, truly a great horror to an athlete impatient to get back to the track, but no problem at all in daily life.

What's more, most running injuries will right themselves automatically after a few days lay-off, though in his natural impatience to go on with his sport and improve his fitness, the runner pesters the doctor or the physio until he has been treated and cured. And why not! It's a fair enough burden on the health service, in the long run highly economic, a veritable stitch in time. The health service could probably treat more than 100 stretched ligaments on the money saved by avoiding just one coronary.

Injuries! In fact every competitive runner, every sportsman, is continually on the edge of injury. During the athletic season of 1985 the cream of Britain's great middle-distance runners, the Crams, Coes, Ovetts and others, were sidelined half the time by these same blighted calf muscles, thigh muscles, ankle tendons and so on.

At veteran level, injury becomes the normal topic of sporting conversation. I often know more of a friend's injuries than I do of his family life. I can tell you just where Ron Franklin's ankle hurt him during his races through the 1970s yet I don't know what he does for a living. I could write a three-volume biography of my own left ham-string; of how that dear muscle was introduced to the violent sport of running in a competition across the beach with my grown-up son when preparing me for my first race in 30 years, how it tore and had to be seen by a dozen medical professionals, of how many years it took to get better, and how it then lived happily ever after.

Injuries! We athletes have 'em like other people have fleas.

We have to learn to live with our injuries, to learn to treat them and, most important, to learn how to avoid them.

You will eventually discover how to deal with minor injuries yourself, from information gleaned off fellow runners, running books and magazines and medical professionals.

Then you'll need to find out how to get the best treatment for injuries that are more serious or are slow to disappear.

But all the time you'll be following the wisest course of sound preparation . . . . of prevention rather than cure.

In the interests of both prevention and cure, it is of value to have an understanding of the causes of the most usual running injuries. These can be summarised, from the point of view of the runner, as follows:

1. Lack of pre-training and pre-race preparation (Warm-up and stretching).
2. Inadequately conditioned muscles. People who take up running as adults often get stiffness or strain at first due to years of underuse of one or other muscle.

3. Accidental injuries. These might come from a fall or a twist.
4. Overuse injuries – wear and tear.
5. Extremes of effort. In your attempts to force the body to its limits of performance one part of it might suffer strain or trauma.

Older runners need to be particularly careful in all these situations. Their muscles are not as supple as those of the youngsters, yet their ability to undergo more punishing training mileage is superior and ironically if they do get injured, it takes longer for their bodies to heal.

First Aid in the Park

However carefully you watch yourself the time will arrive when you do meet a problem and then you may need runner's first aid. Here is a condensed do-it-yourself course, meant to handle the common situation of a pull happening on the run. (If in due course you can't repair it completely, you might need to seek out professional help).

If you are injured while on training, do something about it as soon as possible, not only for the relief of pain but for later full and rapid recovery. Continuing to speed along with a torn leg muscle can only be counter-productive; instead of healing it, you could be doing it worse damage. Nurse the leg – avoid walking more than necessary, let alone running or jogging.

In most cases the best emergency treatment is to apply ice or cold water as early as possible to the skin over the area of the pulled muscle. This has the effect of minimising the internal bleeding, and thus minimising the scar tissue that later forms around the internal wound.

That icing should be done two or three times a day for 48 hours, and during those 48 hours the only other treatment is to rest the affected part, because you don't want to re-open the tear. The ice is applied, for best effect, crushed and wrapped in a cloth to be held against the skin for about ten minutes – and no longer than fifteen. An excellent substitute is a pack of frozen peas, which shapes itself nicely to the leg.

So, for those first 48 hours, the prescription is Ice and Rest, to which should be added Patience – do not agitate to get out running again until the leg is better. I.R.P., better than R.I.P.

Icing alternated with hot splashing is a good treatment for beginning the rehabilitation of the muscle, which benefits from the blood being flushed in and out by the hot and cold applications.

During this second stage the muscle needs to be gently stretched out. (See chapter 12.) When it is properly pliable once more, you must add a strengthening routine to the stretching. You could be ready for this strengthening within a few days or a few weeks, depending on many factors: the severity of your tear, its location, your age and fitness, the time of year, and so on.

Once the muscle is well stretched and strong again, easy running can be started: the pace and distance can be stepped up gradually until you are ready to resume your racing career. Do not hurry the process; impatience and fear of missing the week-end's competition could cost you the season.

You may be successful in curing your injury, or you may not. Often it will disappear out of the goodness of its heart. But what are you to do if you experience continuing pain or disability, and there is nothing for it but medical help?

Runners often find they do not get sympathetic or understanding treatment from their family doctor. Or from a therapist not used to dealing with athletic injuries. It is then advisable to go elsewhere. In my first year of running I met this very difficulty. Mine was a case of injured front of the thigh muscles – from running too fast too soon – and I found myself attending a chiropractor recommended to me by a friend with back pain. This man, amiable enough and learned enough in dealing with postural problems, knew nothing of running injuries. He gave me the usual session on the couch, producing a mighty crack from my spine when twisting it at right angles. It *sounded* convincing, but did nothing for my quadricep muscles.

It was only when I was examined by a doctor of physical medicine, himself a former footballer, who had seen this typical quadricep condition a hundred times before, that I got the right diagnosis and the right treatment, which consisted in stretching and strengthening. Within two days the problem disappeared forever, yet I had borne it for more than a year while touring the rooms of the wrong sorts of expert.

How to find the right sort? A recommendation from a fellow runner is a good start; or a trip to the local general hospital where there is often a sports clinic for out patients; or a cautious enquiry by telephone to the Chartered Society of Physiotherapy, at 14 Bedford Row, London WC2. Tel: 242-1941. The Society holds lists of all physiotherapists in private practice. There is also a sub-branch of physiotherapists interested in sports injuries, The Association of Chartered Physiotherapists in Sports Medicine, c/o D. Chapman, Whiteoaks Clinic, Half Moon Place, Heathfield, Sussex.

Most road runners belong to the AAA Registration scheme. One of its benefits is that it automatically covers members against injuries at races. Some athletic clubs include such a scheme too.

Clinic

Runners and their injuries come in so many shapes and sizes it would need a library of books to deal with all the possibilities of diagnosis and treatment. For yourself it would do no harm to have at least one reference work; the runner's standard volume on the subject is: Vivian Grisogono's *Sports Injuries* (John Murray). Further than that I've picked out a number of the most common of the problems that beset older runners and illustrated them here in the form of actual case histories – these have been selected from the archives of *Running* Magazine. One of them might parallel your own case.

Stitch

Q. As a beginner I suffer particularly from stitch. It usually starts after 2 or 3 miles and is so painful that I have to walk the rest of the way. Is there any way of preventing it, or do I just persevere and hope it goes away?
A. Stitch commonly affects runners. It is often worse if you have eaten just before running. Stitch appears to be the result of tension on the ligament between the diaphragm and the pylorus (the opening from the stomach into the bowels). A stitch may also

indicate lack of fitness, so that it ceases to come on as you become fitter. Sometimes, you may get a stitch from trying to run too fast when you set off, instead of warming up gradually. Another factor can be weak abdominal muscles, so it may be worth strengthening these.

The cure for a stitch depends on the cause. Try not eating within 2 hours of a run; setting off slowly; running on flat surfaces rather than hilly grounds. Once the stitch has come on, it is usually relieved by reducing the tension on the stomach, perhaps by bending forward as you run. Or you may find it helpful to stretch away from the painful side, either while you run, or by stopping to stretch. Relaxed breathing can help reduce the problem, so you could try consciously taking deeper controlled breaths when you feel the stitch coming on.

Puffed

Q. When I jog with my husband I can't help noticing that his breathing is relaxed while I'm puffing and panting, and after a while I get pains in the diaphragm area. Are there any exercises I can do to improve my breathing? Last week I ran 10 miles, was pretty well out of breath the whole time and had pains in my stomach for about 12 hours afterwards. Being 39 probably doesn't help, but my husband is 46 and hasn't been running for so long!
A. If you suffer pains around your trunk when running, and you are short of breath, you should check with your doctor to make sure that there is no medical reason for this. If your doctor declares you fit, the most likely explanation of your problem is that, when running with your husband, you are forcing yourself to run at a faster pace than suits you, and so you are suffering a mild stitch, and your breathing becomes laboured and out of phase. This is something which should improve with training, as increased fitness reduces the effort required to keep all systems going during exercise.

The basis of breathing control is to breathe out for slightly longer than you breathe in: this ensures good gas exchange. When applying this principle to running, the easiest way is to time your breaths with your paces, according to your own rhythm, so that, for instance, you may breathe out for three paces, in for two. You should therefore practise some breathing control, but, more importantly, you should run at a pace that does not keep you struggling for breath, even if it does seem absurdly slow!

Shin soreness

Q. I have been running for about 18 months, and have completed two half-marathons. Two weeks before the second I got severe pains in both shins, so I rested, but successfully completed the event. After that I resumed normal training but the pains recurred. I have since discovered this is the common complaint of shin splints. I rested for a month and did some strengthening exercises. I started running 2 or 3 miles, mainly on grass, about four times a week, but after two weeks the pain returned. What else can I do to cure the problem?
A. At worst, the problem can be a stress fracture in the shin bone, which requires complete rest for at least six weeks. However, when the problem is mild, it is most commonly a strain of the tendons that lie along the inside of the shin bone. One factor in the cause of the problem is excessive running, when your legs are tight in the muscles, through over-training, cramp, or too little recovery time between running sessions. Another factor can be running surface, which can be too hard or too soft.

Most commonly, the problem is related to faulty foot movement during running. If you look at your running shoes, you may find that they have worn down unevenly or incorrectly; normal wear should show that your heel strikes the ground on the outside edge first, and then the pressure is transferred forwards and inwards to the ball of the foot. If you tend to run on your toes, or strike with the inner edge of the heel, you can create abnormal strain on the shin muscles. It is also worth checking that your shoes themselves have not contributed to the problem, either by being worn down, or by being too flared in the heel: this tends to cause excessive roll in the foot during running, and therefore stresses the shin muscles.

The cure would be to identify possible causes of the problem; to rest until your shins only feel mildly sore to the touch; to seek specialist help if necessary, either from a physiotherapist or perhaps a podiatrist, but firstly from your doctor; to continue not only to strengthen but also to stretch the calf muscles; and to do alternative activities in order to keep fit, while avoiding anything that causes pain in the shin.

Finally, when you resume running, you should take care to stretch your leg muscles, especially your calves, before and after your sessions, and to build up your mileage very gradually, allowing rest days between runs, and starting with very short distances.

Strain explained

Q. Please can you tell me the difference between leg 'stiffness' and leg 'strain' particularly in the hamstrings. I would like to know how to avoid these, and what treatment I should use for quick recovery.
A. The difference between leg stiffness and strains is in some cases a question of degree of pain. If you overdo an activity to which your muscles are not accustomed, you will have a feeling of ache, pain and stiffness in those muscles for a couple of days, which will then disappear. However, if you have actually strained a muscle, you are likely to feel a definite sensation of pull or tear on that muscle during the activity with a distinct painful spot afterwards, which hurts to press on, and which hurts when the muscle is made to work.

In the case of the hamstrings, you can feel the tendons clearly on the back of the thighs, extending about halfway up the thigh from the sides of the knee. If any part of these hurts to touch, and that part also hurts if you try to bend the knee against a resistance (e.g. sit on a chair and try to push your heel against the chair leg), or if you extend the hip against a similar resistance, keeping the knee straight, then you know you have a hamstring strain. If so you should avoid stressing the muscle or tendon until the pain has completely gone, as you risk tearing it completely.

The essential cure for strains, and their prevention, is based on regaining full length in the affected muscles. If your muscles are tight, they will be prone to strains and tears. You should be performing a daily routine of static stretching exercises, involving putting the muscles on the stretch and holding the positions, which should feel quite uncomfortable, for a count of 10 without any movement.

105

Q. I am 44 years old and have been running for about six years. I usually train at lunchtime four times a week, with a weekly mileage of around 35mpw when competing. The trouble is that after a long training run or a fast 5M, I am stiff in the leg muscles for about three days afterwards, which prevents me doing anything other than a slow pace.
A. Stiffness after heavy training sessions is to be expected. There are a few measures you can take to overcome the problem when it happens. If your legs are very tight, you should apply ice over them, and then gently stretch all the muscle groups passively to ease them out. You should have a warm bath immediately after your session, and perhaps try to stretch your leg muscles in the bath.

If your programme is properly organised, you should reduce the onset of leg stiffness by getting fitter and stronger. It sounds as though you need to do the type of session which makes you stiff on a more regular basis, although you should never try to repeat a hard session until you have completely recovered from the previous one. All training should be progressive. In mileage training for stamina you are aiming to increase your distance or your speed over a given distance. With fartlek training, you can either increase your speed or the distance of your sprints or the timed intervals. There are limits to the amount you can do. A progressive programme should allow for a build-up over a number of weeks, for instance twelve weeks and then a change of routine.

Stretching and strengthening your legs can help reduce stiffness by increasing their working efficiency. Varying your running surface can also help, as road running alone tends to tighten your legs.

Insoles in your trainers can help to reduce shock and so alleviate stiffness in your muscles.

When you are recovering from tight muscles your first priority is to stretch them passively. Once they are loosened by passive stretching you should try running again, stopping to stretch if they tighten up. You must always remember that a tight, tired muscle is very likely to be strained or torn if you try to work it before it has eased out.

Q. I have a couple of varicose veins in both legs around the shin area. The first few miles of any training run are nearly always painful due to stiffness in the shins, but I usually run the pain off after 2 or 3 miles. Faster than 7 minute miling, the stiffness returns. Is there anything I can do to alleviate the pain?
A. As you only get the pain in your leg veins at the beginning of a run, it would probably help you to do a more efficient warm up before you start running. This would help the circulation in your legs and probably reduce the pain.

It is true that running and exercise are very important in preventing the worst pain of varicose veins. The varicose veins occur because you have two systems of veins in your legs. Those on the surface work at low pressure, but those inside the muscles, which are the deeper veins, work at a higher pressure. Between the two sets of veins you have a connecting system which are called perforator veins. These veins take the blood from the superficial veins to the deep ones. Normally, valves stop the blood from flowing back into the superficial veins as the high pressure of the deeper veins would normally tend to resist the inflow of blood from them, but if the valves are worn out or not working properly, then you tend to have a back flow and the superficial veins become engorged and ultimately painful. If this condition is severe, exercise can make the problem worse because it pumps blood out of the deeper muscles, but if the condition is not at a severe stage (as yours seems not to be) running will help by increasing the circulatory flow in the legs.

You should be sure to stretch your calves carefully before you run and afterwards to retain flexibility in them. If you find you have pain after you run, it may help you to sit with your legs up for a while to help the flow of blood away from your legs.

Calf pain

Q. Twice in the last three months I have suffered what feels like a sharp knife run quickly down the low calf area of my right leg. In both instances these occurred about 48 hours after a competitive Sunday run of about 12 miles. Both injuries have taken

over a week to clear with long walks and a slow build-up on grass to get back into training.
A. If you are worried about your calf pain, you should check with your doctor in case you have a circulatory problem. If you have simply strained the calf muscle, you should be stretching the calf regularly. This means two sessions a day, morning and evening, and before and after every exercise session.

You should also cut down the backs of your running shoes as they may have high heel tabs which create friction on the Achilles tendon which can contribute to calf muscle problems. To cut them down, you should make two vertical slits on either side of where the tendon lies to the level of the back of the ankle. This is normally 2¼" above the upper level of the back of the sole.

You should be careful to check whether you might have shin soreness.

If you have pain on the inner edge of the shin bone where the calf muscle is attached to it, you should rest from running until this has subsided as this condition is potentially quite dangerous.

If you only feel the pain after a hard run, it may help you to put your feet up in the air after these runs and put ice across the calf to help the circulatory flow. Then you should stretch very carefully to keep flexibility in the muscle. If you have a circulatory problem solely related to running, these measures may help to stop the pain developing.

Foot cramp

Q. I suffer painful cramp in both feet and often have to stop to relieve the pain. I wear well-fitting shoes. What is the cause of the problem?
A. You could be drinking insufficient water, or taking too little salt, and so you might be suffering from muscular cramp. Or it is possible that while your shoes fit well while you are at rest, they do not allow room for the expansion of your feet which occurs during exercise. If your toes are cramped at all, they may be forced to work at a mechanical disadvantage, so that the muscles which act on them under the foot feel the strain.

You may alternatively have a condition called plantar fasciitis, in which the long ligament under the foot becomes strained, and therefore painful when it is put on the stretch. The worst possibility is that you have suffered stress fractures in the small bones of your feet, causing spasm in the muscles surrounding those bones. However, since you do not complain of pain at any time other than during running, this is the least likely cause.

Cramp

Q. Thirty kilometres into my third marathon cramp set into my thighs and from then on it was a struggle to the finish. But I felt I had prepared well, and started off gently. I had not suffered cramp in any of my long training runs when I took adequate fluid. On race day I drank before the race and at each of the drinks stations. I'm afraid of doing another marathon until I sort this problem out.
A. Cramp is the normal response of muscle to excessive fatigue. When a muscle group is really exhausted, it stops contracting and relaxing in its usual way, and so jams up into a continual contraction. This hampers your ability to move normally, and, if you are unlucky, the muscle may tear as a result of your efforts to keep it working.

The only way to ease a cramped muscle is to stretch it very carefully, and possibly to rub ice gently over it. Prevention depends on adequate fluid and salts, so you must drink plenty of plain water especially before and during the early stages of your marathon races. Moderate salt on your food is usually enough, but if you suffer repeatedly from cramp, you could try the electrolyte replacement drinks.

The other aspect of prevention is proper conditioning. If the muscle group has sufficient localised endurance and strength training it will be able to work efficiently under stress for longer than if it is not trained. You should examine your training schedule with this in mind. It may be that some hill running would help strengthen your thighs for running, or possibly some interval work to balance your mileage training.

The thighs are particularly vulnerable in marathon runners, because they achieve the main effort of forward propulsion for the leg from your hip. However, one important factor to bear in mind is that 'cramp' in a muscle group can be a protective muscle spasm over a bone injury – in particular a stress fracture.

So if your cramp did not settle down with your recovery period from the marathon, or if you have felt it again on shorter runs, you must check with your doctor in case it is a sign of injury.

Arthritic knees

Q. My GP tells me that I have early osteo-arthritis in both knees. The trouble began when I started to have minor burning sensations and slight tightness of the knee while running. Sometimes on longer runs I felt a rubbing feeling at the top of the shin bone. Since then, I have started doing stretching and strengthening exercises. Perhaps I have not rested or reduced my training as much as I should have, although I have trained more on soft surfaces. Can you supply some background information on arthritis in runners?
A. Osteo-arthritis is not necessarily accompanied by pain, so you should be able to maintain a reasonable amount of running. Equally, overdoing the running will not help your knees, so you must be guided by the pain as to how much you can safely do, and develop alternative methods of keeping fit. It is vital to maintain as much flexibility and strength around the joints as possible. Good substitutes for running, which place far less stress on the knees, are cycling and swimming.

It is important to protect your knees from impact as much as possible, so choose running shoes which are thick-soled, flexible, and well-fitting. Try to run on soft ground or grass as much as possible, and as little as possible on roads. The most important exercise for the knees is simply to brace the knees straight as hard as you can, count to five, then relax completely.

Noisy joints

Q. My ankles always make a loud cracking noise when I flex my feet, such as when walking down stairs. Since taking up running a year ago – I now average 4 miles a day – my ankles have become considerably thicker where the muscles have developed, but they still crack when I walk down stairs or carry out bending exercises for the calves and ankles. It is particularly noticeable first thing in the morning and on the day following a

rest day. **There is no pain associated with this cracking. Is it anything to worry about?**

A. If the clicking noise from your ankles does not give you any pain, we would advise you to ignore it. Many caucasians have noticeable cracking in their joints, which is quite normal, and only means that they have fairly tight ligaments round those joints. Unless there is pain, it is not a problem.

Your ankles have obviously got stronger from running each day. If you do have any discomfort, you should try using insoles for shock absorption, and if these do not help, you should cut down your running, or even rest from running, completely. You could benefit now from doing ankle-strengthening exercises if you are worried about your ankles.

Hamstring strain

Q. During a fairly hard 8 mile session about four weeks ago I felt a pain developing in my right buttock. Two hours after the run it was bad enough for a noticeable lump. I have consulted a physiotherapist who diagnosed muscle spasm. I can now walk much more easily and have tried a mile-and-a-half run although I was very stiff the morning after.

Could you please explain muscle spasm. Can I treat it myself or am I doing more harm than good by exercising? I am 55 years old and have been running for the last eight years, maintaining a 7 minute mile pace and I really miss my sessions.

A. Muscle spasm is a term used to describe a tightening in a muscle. It may be caused by local irritation in the muscle – for instance a tear or strain of muscle fibres, when it is a protective mechanism. Or it may be the result of nerve root irritation referred along the nerve pathways which supply the muscle.

In your case, the buttock pain could be caused by nerve irritation referred from the back, or you may simply have pulled the part of your hamstrings which are attached to the bony part of the buttock. As you have been able to run recently, but have stiffened up after the exercise, I would be inclined to think that yours is a local problem, but if there is any doubt about this, you should refer to your doctor for a medical diagnosis.

If you do have a hamstring strain, you should be gently

111

stretching the hamstring statically to regain full length in the muscle, before you re-start running. To stretch the hamstrings you sit with both legs stretched out in front of you, with your knees straight and gently try to ease your chest down to your thighs, holding your feet if possible, or resting your hands on your ankles. When you feel a pulling sensation at the back of your thigh, you hold the position to a count of 10, then gently let go.

While you hold the stretch, you do not move at all, as any attempts to over-stretch, especially with bouncing movements, will tend to tear the muscles under tension. You should repeat this exercise morning, noon and night, at least six times, until you feel the hurt muscle regain its original pliability. When you resume running you should perform the stretching exercise first of all in your warm-up, and again after your run, to prevent a recurrence of stiffness, which would predispose the muscle to strain and tear. You should gradually build up the amount of running in terms of speed and distance, taking care to maintain flexibility, and avoid stiffness in the muscle at any time.

Black toenail

Q. I have been running between 10 and 20 miles a week with the occasional 40 and 50 for the last year or so. Recently I have been troubled by bruised toenails, mainly on the right foot, with some blackness occurring. My route is over footpaths and includes fairly long, steep hills, both ascending and descending.
A. The problem of toenail bruising is usually related to the fit of your running shoes.

When you try shoes on, you should stand and perhaps jog on the spot in them, as your foot spreads out when it is bearing body-weight. You should have plenty of space in the toe box to wiggle your toes, both up and down, and sideways. This is especially important, as your feet tend to swell on long runs, especially in nylon running shoes, so there must be extra space to allow for this and avoid cramping the toes.

Shoes with a raised heel tend to project the body-weight forward towards the toes during running, and so may aggravate the problem of toenail bruising. It would therefore be better to choose running shoes with full sole thickness from heel to toe. A more important consideration is that shoes with a sole which tends to curl upwards at the toes tend to bring the toe box to a sharp point, thereby creating constriction. This can be seen in the triangular shape of the toe box when the shoe is viewed sideways on.

When your toenails become bruised, it is not usually a serious complaint, Most often, the nail becomes blackened and loose and eventually comes off, after which a new, if rather coarser, nail then grows. The only complication that may easily occur is that of ingrowing toenails, if you are careless about the way you trim your nails. Always cut your nails straight across, not curved.

Bunion runner

Q. Running has done marvels for my general health and well-being. I am 40 and feel younger than I did at 20. I have been running only for about ten months, and have gradually stepped up pace and mileage from 1 mile at nine minutes to various distances between 3 and 10 miles at an average 7:30. My times continue to improve.

My problem is that several years ago I developed a tendency to bunion in the joint above the right great toe. I am also flat-footed. I also discovered that my right hip is slightly higher than the left, and that, surprisingly, my right calf is a half-inch smaller in circumference than the left. Occasionally I get rheumatic feelings in the right hip and in the muscles of the right buttock, especially where these adjoin the leg. I can exaggerate these feelings by tautening the muscles and can ease them by applying pressure at various points between hip and ankles.

When I realised that I possessed a bunion I bought wider fitting shoes. My doctor gave me a prescription for an aspirin-related drug which I didn't take, not wishing to risk internal bleeding. I bought those inserts which you put between your toes, but they kept slipping out. I even tried a 'scientific toe straightener' which was uncomfortable.

It is interesting to note that since I have been running I have had less trouble with the bunion. However, I am concerned that running with a bunion has placed damaging stress on the right leg. On those occasions when I've had a twinge after a long run, it is always in the right ankle or right knee.

What should I do, if anything? Do not ask me to give up running!

A. Besides wearing wide-fitting shoes to help your tendency to a bunion, you should also be sure that your running shoes have a uniformly thick and well padded sole throughout. Most running shoes tend to be thinner under the forefoot, which will undoubtedly aggravate the problem. It might also help you to insert orthotic foot supports into your shoes. The problem in your hip is probably related to a compensatory curve in your back. You should always be careful never to stand with your weight on one leg, or to sit with your legs crossed, as these forms of bad, asymmetrical posture tend to aggravate any imbalance in your pelvis and lower back. Swimming is excellent exercise for maintaining a healthy back and hips. You should also perform suppling exercises to maintain full mobility in your joints.

The twinges you feel in your right leg after running may simply be related to your taking more strain through your dominant side, if you are right-legged and right-handed. They may also be caused by faulty running, in the sense that you may be turning one foot in more than the other while you run, which then creates uneven stresses in the related joints of your leg and back. It is worth checking this on a slow run, and trying to correct to a comfortable and even foot-plant.

Painful knees

Q. I am having trouble with both knee caps just at the side and below the knee, possibly the knee joint. I have had the pain since I started running three months ago. The pain comes on when I run and then for a few days afterwards I just get a twinge of pain if I move awkwardly or press the joints that hurt. I seem to be able to run for about 7 miles before it starts to hurt and I do like to run 13 miles occasionally. The half-marathons that I have run have started out all right but towards the end I had some trouble running and had to walk some of the way. I have tried wearing a different pair of running shoes but it hasn't made any difference. All my doctor could suggest was to give up running; he did not even examine my knees. I have tried knee strengthening exercises but these have not helped.

114

A. Your main problem seems to be your impatience! You have built up to relatively long runs in only three months. The same applies to specific knee strengthening exercises, they can only be of benefit if you do them regularly and intensively for at least six weeks, and if at the same time you stop doing any pain-inducing activities, such as running.

It is not clear exactly where your knees hurt. Pain over the front of the knee in runners is usually directly due to problems in the knee-cap joint. This is generally cleared by the correct exercises, in conjunction with avoiding any painful activities. Pain to the side of the knee is usually due to the iliotibial tract friction syndrome.

If, however, your knees swell up, you must check back with your doctor, as you probably ought to have an examination by an orthopaedic specialist. Knee pain can be due to faulty foot mechanics, or unsuitable shoes. If you notice uneven wear on your shoes, or a tendency to wear down the inner edges of your soles, it may be worth consulting a podiatrist for a biomechanical assessment of your foot movements during running.

Try to identify the nature of your knee pain, which may necessitate asking your doctor to refer you to an orthopaedic specialist. You should stop running for the moment, although you could substitute crawl swimming. You should continue with the specific knee exercises appropriate for your knee: it is usually essential to do straight-leg strengthening exercises for most knee conditions.

12 A STRETCH IN TIME

Stretching is without doubt the most important discipline to be observed by a runner. For an Over 40 runner it should feature even higher than that – one above the top! Such a runner's muscles and tendons need the most devoted nursing.

Whether you are racing or training, running or jogging, doing short or long distance, you should be hanging in there beforehand stretching out the muscles and limbering up.

What are the benefits of stretching?

1. It protects the muscles from damage by keeping them supple.
2. It lengthens out the muscles to give longer reach and strengthens them for higher speed.

Who could resist a regime with attractions like that? Yet the majority of runners can't get round to it! It's not that the actual stretching schedules aren't easy enough in themselves, it's that hardly anyone has got the willpower. Very much like small boys and their toothbrush drill, they'll even deliberately waste time pretending instead of actually doing.

Yes, it's New Year Resolutions all round.

Make stretching and the associated warm-up your religion, never to be left aside.

Whether the weather appears too cold or too hot, if you're going to be running more than a mere toddle get in a few minutes of stretching on your most vulnerable muscles. I would do as a warm-up a half mile of very slow jogging, before the stretching, to reduce the risk of a minor tear. When the muscle is quite cold it tends to be stiff and brittle and a jerky movement could have an undesirable effect. The effort of jogging gently warms up the muscles as well as the runner and actually makes the muscles more plastic and pliant.

The warm-up not only protects the muscles from damage, but it also prepares them for stretching and consequently lengthening. Furthermore the warm-up has its own speed-raising powers, because it sends the blood powering round the body, to hype up brain as well as muscles.

The sprinter has a particular need for a warm-up because he runs fastest when already pouring with sweat before a race; he works himself up into a kind of high-speed trance. Sprinters will do first a kind of walking-pace jog. Then the stretching, then some speedier action: a few strides, a few bursts, a few blasts out of the blocks. By now the body should be on the tarmac ready to take off.

If there's a wait needed before the competition, a sprinter keeps that warmth topped up. I sat opposite the start of the 100 metres at the Moscow Olympics and noted with approval how the British sprint team, led by Allan Wells, came out to the main track from the warm-up track wrapped up in two complete sets of track suits – though the temperature in the stadium was in the 80s.

The distance runner doesn't find it necessary – nor maybe possible! – to steam up to that extent, but needs a good long slow warm-up. Many an old cross-country veteran prowls beforehand around the whole course though he may have run it yearly for the last two or three decades. A distance runner often finds it hard to summon up race speed until the body has ground out quite a bit of mileage, until well into his second wind, even his third.

It's not usually necessary to bully or persuade people to get in their warm-up – for most it's an enjoyable period. But the stretching! Ah – you must bully yourself, if you can't hire a ready-made bully; and as a veteran with stiffer tendons to your muscles, it's more important than ever before.

Here, now, are some of the routines to limber up with. When you do them get your mind thinking deep into the muscles as you flex them. Spend up to 15 minutes on the warm-up and 15 on the exercises.

After your jog this is a suggested schedule, combining warm-up exercises with the actual stretching routines.

Start from the top of the body, at the neck, and work down

117

wards. This is useful if only because it reminds you mechanically just where you are at any moment. So now for it.

The neck

Stand with feet together and arms down your side and, first of all slowly, rotate the head around the body in the biggest circle possible. Keep it relaxed so that it almost lolls, meanwhile feeling your way into the muscles, giving them a nice old stretch. Do a half dozen of the slow rotations in each direction, then do another set faster, once there's no danger of ricking the neck through too sudden a start.

Shoulders

Standing straight up, feet together, arms at the sides, hunch your shoulders around together, keeping the rest of the body relaxed. First hunch clockwise twenty times, then anti-clockwise the same number. It's a kind of rotating shrug you're after, with the arms and hands dangling idly.

Arms

Windmill the arms. Take one arm at a time, clench the fists lightly, swing them as close to your ears as possible and keep swinging 20 times, then in the opposite direction.

Trunk

Arms clasped behind the neck, legs planted well apart, rotate the upper part of the body to make sweeping movements downwards and outwards and around. Half a dozen slow, then in the other direction, then half a dozen fast, and the other direction.

Hamstrings

These are the long muscles at the back of the thighs. The easiest exercise to take on board is simple toe-touching, but leave this out if you have a suspect back. When toe-touching, you genuinely

118

need to stand there with knees locked, back straight and hang out; let the body gradually pull you down, don't force it. Think into every muscle again, feel the hamstrings slowly pay out as you dangle there. At the bottom, keep your fingers on the floor and rock your backside from side to side, like a friendly hound, transferring some of the tension to the tendons at the side of the buttocks. But remember, as in other exercises, no bouncing, just long drawn-out stretches. Use the arms to do the pulling, let the hamstrings be stretched.

Quadriceps

(The long muscles on the front of the thigh.) Stand with feet together, lift the left foot behind you and grab it with the left hand, at the ankle, then pull it up behind you, so that the back of your shoe is tucking into your buttocks. Keep the upper part of the left leg pointing vertically downwards still – your left leg is now doing a hairpin, with knee pointing to the ground. Meanwhile you're trying to keep your balance standing on the right leg alone – concentrate on what you're doing and you'll find that easier.

Hold, feeling the tension in that long muscle of the left upper thigh, for 30 seconds. Then the other leg.

The Muscles of the inner thigh

(The Adductors) Sitting on the floor with your knees straight and legs stretched as far apart as possible, gently bend forward from the hips, keeping your back straight, until you feel the pull on the inside of your thighs. Hold the position for a count of 20, then relax.

The calf muscles

Stand facing a wall, your feet planted on the floor a yard away. Lean forward, keeping your feet in place, until your palms are against the wall at head height and attempt to push it down. You are now leaning at about 45°. All the while keep your knees locked and your shoes flat on the ground, until you feel the pull on the calves. Concentrate on feeling the effort there and hold for a count of 20.

That's a simple programme, which can be done whenever you have a spare moment; waiting for a bus, maybe. I'm looking forward to the time when the bus shelters of the land are full of people stretching. Well, what do *you* do when waiting for a No. 31? My osteopath friend, Donald Norfolk, author of *Farewell to Fatigue,* has prescribed a stomach routine to be carried out at the bus stop: slowly suck in the stomach until it's reached the back bone, relax, then in and out 20 times . . . . of great value for the back, and nobody will notice what you're up to. Break each stretching exercise down into two stages, first an easy stretch then a full stretch which can be held a little longer.

There are of course other parts of the body that can be stretched and dozens of other suitable exercises for each part, but you've got to stick to a minimum selection to be practical. I believe my own coach, Peter Halstead, has a large enough repertoire of stretches to keep seven maids with seven brooms stretching out from the time they become vets until they turn 80. To vary the mix of exercises helps with the enjoyment. It also adds to the value of the stretching for a different exercise will stretch a muscle at a slightly different angle; thus the sum of several almost similar exercises does a more comprehensive job on the particular muscle being treated.

To illustrate the crucial importance of observing the warm-up and stretch routines before every race, here is . . . .

The Story of a Runner who Didn't

How fate was to serve the renowned Jack Williams . . . . a moral tale with a bitter sting . . . . of his confidence that he would bring home the first world gold in his event . . . . of how confidence became over-stretched . . . . and the muscles under-stretched . . . . the price extracted being a pound of flesh, instead of gold!

Jack Williams was one of that band of runners who have broken records yet never become world champion. I always think of valiant Jack during the warm-up session; a bulky man, looking altogether the true and portly Sir Jack Falstaff when he wrapped himself up cosily – when he deigned to, I should add.

It was the First World Veteran Championships, at Toronto, Canada, 1975, and there was a very useful British team with several medal hopes going along, including jolly Jack.

We had a week first in Upstate New York, at a new-laid track in the town of White Plains. Jack and Mavis Williams were with the rest of the international party at college campuses nearby. 'Come on, my son!' was heard for the first time at this track. It was the great cockney runner, Jack Williams, in his role as spectator, urging on the other British competitors.

Jack, in the days before professionalism became respectable, had worked things so that he was all but a professional runner – he worked at the Inland Revenue, who allowed him to spend much of his time running! This was a nice arrangement for Jack, and for Mavis, who had taken up running herself lately to keep him company on his outings . . . . and no doubt very gratifying for the British tax-payer.

It was also in the days before distance running had become the only kind of running anyone understood, and Jack was a sprinter. Today he would be a *mere* sprinter, but then he was a special hero.

The programme ahead was a preliminary week of races at New York, followed by a week at Toronto, and Jack intended to be the first ever world champion in his events, the 100m and 200m for men aged 65 and over. By tremendous luck and timing he turned 65 in the plane coming over from Gatwick, and was thus the youngest and best placed in the class by age. He was best placed too by his form. 'I'll toddle it,' he announced to all while taking a birthday drink. A confident man, Jack.

At New York he had a first look at the entries on the programme and repeated: 'I'll toddle it. The best competition must be Carnine and Caruso . . . . no problem.'

'Oh, come on, Jack,' demurred Mavis, showing him a page from the world rankings book. Both the Americans, Carnine and Caruso, and also a German, Busch, had been credited the previous year with 13.4 seconds for 100m.

'I've done under 13,' Jack snorted. Mavis, a quiet woman, but decided, noted: 'That was two years ago.'

Another snort: his complete response, except for some derogatory remarks about the 'generosity' of U.S. time-keeping, compared to the unbending accuracy of the British.

'Well, Jack,' said Mavis politely, 'I remember the conditions were very windy that day you went under 13: a following wind.'

'I have to toddle it,' forecast Jack, ignoring the wind.

It was ideal weather, certainly for the sprinters: hot, dry and still. You could get up a sweat in a few strides down the track. Nonetheless I knew that I had to nag Jack to prepare himself. When I arrived at the championships I started my own stretch, bending over to count up my toes, while grunting at Jack from the level of my knees: 'Get yourself really warm, man, and don't forget the stretching.'

But sprinters are essentially impatient characters, not to be bothered by hanging around and preparing themselves. They want to be out of the blocks and racing; they're flyers by nature. So, although Jack cheerfully agreed to put in some stretching, after a very few perfunctory bounces he found it necessary to attend to a suddenly arising crisis elsewhere on the track, in a 10,000m race – a dour battle in the sun. The lap-scoring had gone very wrong; in a field of thirty runners chasing each other around, some a lap or more behind others, the officials had become confused about who had done exactly what and the runners were all putting in their own contrary claims with their last breaths.

Naturally this all took Jack's attention – he wasn't able to avoid butting in, to show the Americans how we British did that sort of thing.

So he set off for his own race not properly prepared.

Nevertheless, aided by the sun and the high-grade competition we were all setting personal bests, and Jack at 65 left Caruso and Carnine and a third speedy American, Castro, well behind on the straight, to take the 100m gold in precisely 13 seconds (and no comments about over-generous American time-keeping!). A world record for the age.

At the end of the week of competition in White Plains our whole party trans-shipped to Toronto, to settle into university campuses again, and to race in the first World Veteren Championships, at the Etobicoke track, a worn-out rubbery affair set on a little suburban hillock.

'Old age is catching up with me,' announced Jack Williams before the start. There were to be six days for the championships; for Jack heats, semi-finals and finals, a race a day for three days, the 100m series first, then the last three days for the 200s.

'Don't be silly, Jack,' said Mavis primly.

'I'm a week older than when I set the world record,' he winked, 'but never mind, I'll toddle it again.'

The weather was still hot, but not so beneficial somehow; humid and enervating. It certainly put Jack off any sensible warm-up programme, or any protective stretching procedures. We had a little wordless dialogue between us. From the stands I wagged a finger at him to where he stood around on the track; he pointed up at the hot sun and shrugged his shoulders.

The truth was that he didn't feel he needed to extend himself too greatly in the first round, the heats, to qualify for the semi-final. He had achieved a time a second better than any of those drawn against him in his heat and probably didn't need the extra advantage that a warm-up could give one.

They lined up, this international batch of grandfathers, in four heats: Jack in one, Carnine in one, Caruso in one and Busch in one. Good seeding; the proper objective of picking heats is to split the favourites off from each other, so making it more likely that they will meet in the later stages and push one another to make a real race of the final.

Jack's heat was too easy for him, really, but he didn't feel this mattered, and at the blast of the gun charged down the straight in a very relaxed way, like an amiable buffalo, sparing a moment to look over at the stands and generally show off rather. Mavis, who felt it was her task to see that the world championship gold medal was brought back for the Williams trophy stand, was caused to say in a severe way, 'Come on really, Jack,' below her breath.

Half way along the track you could see Jack become aware of pursuit. Yards behind him still but making a heavy pattering, another bulky sprinter was coming along – a complete unknown in fact, a fun-runner, a no-hoper, but his clattering was enough to rouse Jack. There was no doubt Jack wanted to be first in his heat, if only for the look of things, to make a statement, if you like, to lay down firmly who was master – for glory!

So he stepped on the gas. He suddenly accelerated; you could see his big muscles at the back of the leg, the hamstrings, dig in. What a force this explosive movement puts on the hamstrings!

It was too much of a force for Jack's, they simply weren't supple

123

enough. Caught off guard like this, the left hamstring took the path of least resistance – it tore. You could see it happen, you could even hear something go 'ping'. And you could observe Jack's left hand clutch at the back of the thigh; he slowed down into a kind of sprinting limp.

Was he done for? Mavis was terrified, we all gasped. However his momentum carried him over the line, though he was passed before the tape by the man who'd seemed to threaten him during the race. Okay, no real harm done, he had qualified for the semi-finals, if not with the same high degree of honour.

But he looked awkward coming off the track. He was hobbling. Naturally when you pull a big hamstring muscle, bits of the muscle are frayed, the muscle loses some of its elasticity, it hurts, and you hobble like a haltered horse. You can't set the leg down comfortably, you certainly can't thrust it into action with the usual force; and the body instinctively favours its handicapped member, for fear of its ripping some more.

Jack, with his coach Mavis helping him along, went off to look for medical treatment, to get himself patched up for the semi-final the next day: the British team had no physiotherapist. Jack wandered around the basement of the Etobicoke stand, the changing-room area, until he found a bench to lie face-down on, and tried to instruct Mavis in massaging the leg. I sought him out to say that the German team physio was offering to put in some work on the injury.

He was very suspicious somehow; nevertheless things were too critical to turn down any assistance. The physio, Karl-Heinz Reuther, worked away on him. The first thing he said, in his classic German accent, as he kneaded Jack's thigh muscles, was 'Vy didn't you stretch more? I think you didn't stretch sufficient, no?'

Jack growled. Those despicable Germans!

He got ice-pack treatment, to stop the blood flowing in the area of the tear, and gentle massage and rest all day. While the remainder of the games were going on up at the track, Karl-Heinz and Mavis and Jack sweated it out in the dank treatment room. The weather was as hot and humid as anything we'd come across, and the treatment room was its extreme expression. Nevertheless it wasn't a bad environment for muscles, which like to be warm and flexible.

124

So they worked all day and then Jack and Mavis were sent off to their student bed-sitter for the night and told to report in again next morning before his semi.

'Did he advise you to stretch?' I asked a bit tactlessly.

'No,' growled Jack.

'No,' explained Mavis, 'no stretching for 48 hours after a tear.'

In the morning the physio after an inspection thought carefully about his diagnosis and then asked Jack: 'When is your next race after the 100?' What he was trying to convey was the decision that Jack had no earthly chance of running that day; but later, perhaps a day or two further down the programme, he could make it, maybe.

So the 100m medal was gone. For the rest of this second day Jack continued with his treatment while the semi-finals were being run. Caruso won the one, and Carnine the other, with the German Busch very close behind in spite of having stumbled at the start. 'Diabolical,' came in a muffled kind of congratulatory grunt from the treatment room.

The German physio had gone up to watch that race with Busch in it, leaving Jack to work up some plot in his head about how he had obviously planned the whole thing, including Jack's original hamstring tear.

Jack lying there in a mournful pose was rejoined by a cheerful physio who reassured him; 'Vere dere's life dere's hope.' Jack forbore to snort, but pointed impatiently down to his injured leg, as if to say: 'Get on with it.' The physio gave him a hearty dig in the belly of the hamstring. This made Jack wince in spite of himself. 'Ja,' the physio noted owlishly, 'she not too damn good yet.'

The third day and it was the 100m finals, with the eight fastest Over 65 men preparing to contest for the medals. This time Jack bravely hobbled up the stands to sit beside Mavis and croak 'Come on, my son,' as Carnine raced across the line in 13.5 seconds, ahead of Caruso, Busch and the others. Everyone knew what he thought of such a time, he the holder of the world record at 13 seconds.

The next day was scheduled for the first round of the 200m event. Jack needed to qualify again here, naturally, in order to go further and stand a chance to reach the finals.

But no, he didn't need a word from the physio to tell him how unwise it would be. He could have hobbled it, possibly, injuring the muscle still more, and at a galumphing sort of speed that would have left him trailing. So he had to withdraw from the rest of the championships. He didn't take very kindly to a friendly warning from the physio to be sure and warm-up and stretch in the future whenever there was fast running afoot.

So it was that Jack Williams lost his chance of a world gold though ten years later his time of 13 seconds still stands as the British record, if not the world. Even the amazing Colin Fairey of Kettering failed to beat it when in the Over 65s. This next year or two, I know of at least three British runners who will be making the attempt – Les Williams, Alan Bowdler and myself.

Nor was Jack able to have a go, subsequently, at the Over 70 record, for he died aged 69. His widow Mavis, who followed him into world sprinting, will, I hope, attempt the Women's Over 70 one of these days. 'Come on, me gal!'

13   FIT FOR LIFE

There is fitness . . . . and there is fitness. The word has a whole range of meanings; even the kind of physical fitness we runners talk of has a whole range of attributes. You have to decide just which and how much of it you want for yourself.

As a runner you will anyway be achieving the most vital of the lot, cardiovascular fitness, the kind that will keep your heart and lungs healthy and your coronaries at bay. This comes through the training effect of aerobic exercise. The minimum amount of exercise you need to provide this effect is surprisingly low; continuous jogging for 25 minutes, a few times a week. That is said by researchers to give you a strong and healthy heart muscle. Few runners fail to exceed that sort of weekly mileage in the ordinary way of business.

But after all people are not looking solely for protection against early death, foremost in importance though that may be. They want insurance against the effects of neglect too, and still further they may be eager for positive fitness, the sort that makes you feel and look a million dollars.

To keep you in all-round tip top condition, providing those extra benefits, you need to incorporate into your scheme regular fitness training in the gym, as well as the running. You'll need it too if you race at international level and want to *earn* a million dollars!

What does 'all-round' condition comprise in addition to the soundness of the heart muscle? Simply all-round muscle tone, which will provide a framework for the soundness of the rest of your equipment, the very bones and joints and vital organs.

For instance back problems, which afflict millions among the middle aged, can be reduced through the strengthening of the back and stomach muscles. Arthritis and the loss of bone mass with age can be forestalled by exercise, and even general physical coordination can be improved through the work done in the gym.

In a phrase, if you look after your muscles they will look after the rest of you.

Let us summarise all this in a small table, defining your possible personal needs from fitness in ascending order and the prescribing systems to achieve them:

A. To help prevent sudden death or chronic illness from heart disease.

B. To ward off ill-health generally and disability.

C. To reach superb condition . . . . and get that tingling feeling all over.

If you're ready to settle for A, routine jogging is the answer. If you want B you need jogging plus fitness training. But if you want still more, C, you need jogging plus fitness training plus weight training.

If you're aiming still higher than this level, to some world of Ds, Es and Fs, to procure for you elaborate biceps and a stomach to drive a bus over, in a quest to see how far the middle-aged spirit can be driven, you're going to have to move full-time into the gym. Don't look to the chewing of fibrous foods, or sitting up straight in your chair or yoga to bring you to this state of grace!

Fitness training, even at the moderate B level, takes a fair amount of time, because it has to include a preliminary warming-up and stretching period – and that cannot be hurried through. The muscles and tendons must be warmed-up and made pliable before you work on them, as if you were dealing with a lump of plasticine. The limbs are going to be extended and rotated, and heaved frightfully ho, up and around and to and fro, and they will not want to have the associated muscles and the tendons that lash them together torn or snapped in the process, which they might do when cold and brittle. Remember the body at this time should be undergoing extremes of efforts in order for you to benefit; fitness exercises must be done with a will.

In a fitness class the stretching session gradually merges into the warm-up and the warm-up into the big exercises. Perhaps 20 minutes is needed for the preliminaries and half an hour for the main work-out.

Then, if you're going on to level C, the weights will absorb another half hour.

A Place for Fitness

How do you provide a fitness set-up for yourself? You can do it at home, or you can join a class.

You have to be a very lucky person and extremely persevering to make it work in your own home. It isn't just the space needed or the solidity of floor or the expensive equipment – it's the will-power. To do a full hour at the appointed time every week, to take yourself through an elaborate repertoire of exercises, and, hardest of all, to bully yourself into doing them at the limits of your ability, is a daunting task.

Soon it happens that you 'don't feel like it,' or '10 minutes should do tonight,' or you chicken out after eight repetitions instead of twelve – and yet it's those last four that really count, that send the blood surging through the muscles to build them up into bonny big fellows.

And how to note whether your legs are waggling from side to side above you symmetrically enough? And who to advise on a new set of variations to get at a specific one of the hundreds of muscles the human body is blessed – or afflicted – with?

By far the best is to join a class and then, to search out, not a kindly, considerate coach, but one notorious for his determination to leave you at the end of the session sizzling away in a pool of your own sweat.

I have gone to and enjoyed the local class conducted by Peter Halstead for ten years, partly for his virtuoso teaching but most of all for his ability to keep me at it long after I might have given up. The body says 'No,' but the brain says 'Go on,' Dr Gradgrind Halstead calls out remorselessly and I manage just one more clean-and-press. 'Come on Sylvester, get up off the floor.' Yet at home with my own equipment, I can't persuade myself to do a worth-while session more than two or three times a year. When you know you have a class to attend you make sure to get there.

Peter himself spends most days working out. In his early 40s he is in excellent shape of course, though he confesses that his main purpose in all this hard work at keeping fit is to prepare himself for a lifetime of regular gourmet meals, taken with the best of wines.

Fitness classes come cheap and dear. The cheap ones are those set up by local authorities; a call to the recreation department should help you locate one. They'll often be mixed, men and women, young and old.

At the other end of the scale there are plush clubs, with halls full of machinery, jacuzzi baths and poolside bars. Excellent if you have the few hundred pounds a year for membership. The mass movement towards fitness has, however, begun to create the need for a more economical type of club and you can expect them to proliferate in the next two or three years.

The coach at the fitness centre will have his own plan: he will no doubt order a brisk few minutes of jogging on the spot or the like for warming up, then he will have you attack each part of the body in turn, starting with the neck and shoulders and making a journey down past the stomach and the back to the hips, legs, ankles and even toes.

If you're doing weights, he will again probably start with the upper body then work you over down to the back and legs.

In your first week or two you will almost certainly feel a degree of stiffness some 36 hours after your session if you have worked willingly enough. This is not at all serious; gentle jogging should help it to dissolve away before the next time, and by the third or fourth week it will have gone, although any new exercises on a new part of the body could produce another mild bout of stiffness. Don't be put off.

At home basics

As it may be necessary in spite of this for you to tackle do-it-yourself fitness – perhaps you have suffered a temporary injury and the physio advises you to exercise indoors – I will outline a few simple exercises that can be undertaken at home.

First of all I would advise making do with the minimum of equipment. I am no believer in the indoor bicycle-machine or rowing-machine. They are boring to use; bought in a fit of ambition they are stashed away after two or three efforts – the cycles are not provided with wheels so you can't ride them to work and the rowing machines won't float.

Buy a rubber mat, 8'×4', to jump up and down on, and wear your ordinary training shoes. If you propose to tackle weights, a

130

basic barbell system can handle virtually any proposition, but see my advice below.

For stretching exercises return to the previous chapter; in this chapter there are strengthening routines, to be sandwiched between stretching and weights. If you need more than the sample presented, ten thousand different and wonderful routines exist and can be picked up from magazine articles, books or friendly coaches.

Weights, though, are not as easy to learn on your own at home. Even the expert weightlifter will choose not to work out at home when operating with heavy weights, for safety's sake.

To act as a dreadful warning, here is the story of a vet who'd been ordered off the roads by his physio, so that he might rest his injured and overworked Achilles tendons. He was told to go to a weights class to keep in trim during the period when he would miss out on his running.

He was a restless fellow, impatient to resume running, and found the rather gentle rate of progress at this class somewhat frustrating, so he rigged up an apparatus at home, a wooden barrel stuffed with bricks, for doing 'deadlifts', straightleg lifts to the shoulder while bending forward.

Unfortunately he overdid the weight of bricks in his inexperience and next day found himself with severe muscle pulls at the tops of his hamstrings. He was obliged to stow the painful hamstrings in his car and drive them back to the physio. Here the diagnosis was that he had overindulged in the deadlifts, virtually pulling the upper parts of the muscles out of their sockets in the seat of the pants.

He was given four weeks complete lay-off, then a further period of fitness and weight-training only – but still no running.

Again he found the weights class too slow, so to give himself extra effort this resourceful fellow rigged up a pulley wheel from a projecting beam outside the balcony of his third floor flat, hoisted up the barrel, again filled with bricks, and tied it off there. After that he returned to the ground and untied the rope, so that he could lower the barrel to the ground, before heaving it up again. He intended to do a dozen repetitions of heaving up and lowering down the barrel, to keep his shoulder muscles toned up.

But again he miscalculated the number of bricks he could

manage. So as the barrel started down it jerked him off the ground, so fast and so far that he was afraid to let go. Halfway up, he met the barrel coming down and it gave him a nasty knock on the shoulder.

He then continued to the top, banging his head against the beam and getting his fingers jammed in the pulley. At that moment, the barrel hit the ground, bursting its bottom, and allowing the bricks to spill out. He was now heavier than the barrel, and he started down again at high speed. Halfway down he met the barrel coming up and received injuries to his ankles. When he hit the ground he landed hard on the bricks, getting some painful bruises on his chest from the sharp edges.

At this point he lost his presence of mind and let go of the line. The barrel then came whistling down again, giving him another blow on his back thigh muscles as he lay there. This naturally necessitated another call on the physio. What should he do, he croaked?

The physio was not at all concerned over the cuts and bruises. 'You can go back to hard hillwork runs this evening,' said the laconic man,' and some 400s on Thursday. And see you don't overdo the weights.'

Basic Exercise Routines

Sit-Ups

There are a dozen different variations of this standard exercise alone. Preferred by me is the sit-up where your feet are hooked under a low bar or held at the ankles and your knees are bent. The hands should be clasped at the back of the neck, with the elbows pointing forward, so that as you come up steadily, from the lying back to the sitting position, you can reach out to the tops of the knees with the elbows.

Then you go down on your back again and keep on, up and down, for 10 repetitions. Take a half minute's rest, then repeat the 10 sit-ups; take another rest, and do 10 last sit-ups.

If you can't manage all that the first time, do 6 instead of 10, but don't give up. Fight against any readiness to surrender. Ignore the hot pain in the stomach. That's the mark of success. Some people will manage more at their first attempt, but everyone should keep pushing to a new effort.

Once you have the ability to do three steady sets of 25, go for speed. In my own class we have a weekly competition, and aim for personal bests, in a flat-out two minutes. The record is 140, an unbelievable pace, and there is a woman runner in her mid-thirties who has managed 125. (As a matter of engineering and anatomical fact, a woman finds sit-ups comparatively easy, for she is endowed with a good, heavy base to rock on, yet has a lighter shoulder structure to be lifted up and down)

Press-ups

Here women don't have it so good, for the shoulders have to do the work of carrying the whole body, bottom and all, up and down. For this exercise, you lie facing down on your mat, with the hands pressing on the floor just underneath the shoulders. Keeping the whole of the body and legs in a nice straight line, you lift until your arms lock out. Let yourself down again until you are nearly lying on the floor, then start the second press-up immediately, in a smooth rebound.

The same sort of routine is required as for sit-ups: three sets of 10 repetitions each, thus 30 in all. It may take the untrained person longer to reach this point, but once reached, try for more, for a new Everest. A harder variation can be attempted – clapping the hands together before allowing the body to return to the horizontal. This is a knack that can soon be picked up, and has benefits in searching out extra muscles. If you find this too easy . . . . clap your feet together too, at the time you're clapping the hands. You will feel very pleased with your control of the body when you learn this.

Women often need a little concession here, because they are now in the situation of having to lift the heavier part of their structure with the less powerfully constructed part. They may do the press-ups with the knees as the lowest point, instead of the toes.

Leg chops

Here you lie back on your elbows making sure the flat of your back is on the ground and, keeping your legs straight, lift them

133

alternately in the air, allowing them to come down to within an inch of the floor, though not actually to touch it. You could start with 20, and work up within a few weeks to a full 100. This is good medicine for the stomach muscles.

Burpees (or Squat Thrusts with an upward jump)

More difficult to describe this than to do, though most people will have seen them on *Superstars*. From a standing position, jump upwards, dropping in an uninterrupted movement into a crouching position, leaning on straight arms with knees tucked under. Then thrust the legs backwards to bring you into the classic press-up position. Next, return in a single vigorous movement to the crouching position. Jump up high from the crouch, dropping again into the crouch to repeat the exercise. Do 10 times, working up in due course to 25.

The Big Mix

Once you've mastered the above four they can be joined together to make one continuous killer sequence. The sequence must be done in this order: burpees, sit-ups, press-ups, leg chops, so that you keep having to turn around from a facing-the-floor position to backs-to-the-floor, just to make it harder. Here is the whole thing: do 10 of the first exercise straight off without a pause, then follow it, still without any pause at all, with 10 of the next and so to the end. Now, still without a pause, go through the whole cycle of 10 burpees, 10 sit-ups, 10 press-ups, 10 leg chops all over again. In fact do altogether four complete cycles without a stop. It's a killer all right, and will make the centrepiece of the evening. It's customary when finishing this one to shake the head doubtfully as if to say 'We must be mad to do it.' That's a way of expressing a great self-satisfaction.

Jack Knife

Lie on the back and swiftly reach out with your fingers to touch the toes, which in turn are trying their best to come up to meet the fingers. You end up in a circle on the small of your back. Then straighten out flat on the back, then up again. The usual 10 repetitions. You must keep the arms and the legs perfectly straight: the exercise needs to be performed with style.

Jumping Jack Knife (not for beginners)

Now you're standing up straight to start with. You jump up in the air, and at the same time reach, as above, to touch toes to fingers. As you land back on the floor, straighten up with hands in air. Do 10 jump-ups without pause.

This is just a taste from a vast repertoire of exercises. Insert a few variations you have researched here and there, to keep your interest fresh; for you must find this fun yourself whatever agonies the body may experience.

As time passes even the body will reluctantly start to enjoy it, and you yourself will find a tremendous sense of well-being in the days following the session. I can promise you that. I first looked out a fitness course for myself when afflicted with a torn calf muscle and ordered by the clinic not to run but to keep my form up through swimming or exercise. I found the swimming pleasant enough, but it was difficult to pile in sufficient hard work to get the training effect or even to maintain general muscle condition. The fitness class did it; then I simply kept on forever, even once the calf was right again.

A last reminder: when at your exercises, do them as hard as you can; there's no percentage in merely going through the motions to complete the programme. Put all your effort into it, at the expense of grunting and groaning inelegantly. No pain, no gain!

14 RISKS FOR RUNNERS

In the alarmist view there are a good number of dangers that lie in wait for the runner. On examination however, many of these turn out to be imaginary, a few trivial and only one or two worth serious attention.

Running injuries, already dealt with in Chapter 11, lead the list of the molehills that have been magnified into mountains. Injuries come and go, they affect your running though not much else, and they are thus no real danger, merely an acceptable minor risk.

What you should seriously take up guard against is *overdoing* your running, which can have unpleasant consequences, the worst of which is that if you become obsessive about the sport, you could find yourself caught up by reaction and apathy, and in the end not a runner any more! I've seen it happen: someone has successfully gone past the Six Week Barrier, then become positively high on zeal, unable to stop themselves. They train twice every day and race twice every week, mile after mile, fixture after fixture. No lay-off, not even at holiday time . . . . then comes a tweak in an ankle, a foolhardy continuation through the pain and finally enforced rest.

That resting period is when reaction might arrive; it sets in good and strong so that even when the ankle is fully healed, the runner sits tight, for all the first fine careless rapture has been drained to the bottom.

There are of course people who can cope with never-ending sessions and seasons of training runs and races, but they are found mostly in the ranks of the case-hardened, life-long runner, not the new breed. My friend Ron Franklin of the Thames Valley club would qualify for a world record for overdoing it in long-distance racing. From his schoolboy days and career as a Welsh international and later as a distinguished vet he has kept it up unflaggingly. Today still, in his late 50s, he rarely through the twelve months misses twice-weekly racing, perhaps a 1500m Open Meeting event on the Wednesday, then a 5000m on the Saturday, or a 10-mile and a half-marathon back-to-back at the weekend.

So it goes throughout his season, which lasts from January 1 to December 31 – every season. He and I calculated once that he had run the equivalent of twice round the world. In fact he's flown or motored many times round the world to get to these races. In his career Ron has been injured many a time, but due to his years of toughening up no lasting harm has come to him.

It is the novice runner that needs the warning. The first practical step you can take is to be very firm about the minimum one day a week of rest – never transgress; it's worth another mention here. What's more, don't undertake too many races for their own sake; rather aim at an occasional big target and ignore the temptation to use minor races en route as training. Keep your racing for maximum effort and training for training.

It is particularly important to stop all running when injured or ill, especially if the illness is of a viral nature, such as flu. Then wait until you are quite recovered; runners at all levels can come to harm by exercising or stressing themselves when not fully recuperated. I have known men and women so seriously run down through this cause that they have in the end taken as long as a year to get properly well and right back to form. A few more days of proper convalescence would have saved them all those missed months.

Ole Rockin' Chair

In 1984 the campaign to cry up running injuries was stepped to the morbid limit. This was on the occasion of Jim Fixx's collapse and death on the road.

Could there have been a greater anomaly than that of a man who had saved people's lives through getting them out running having his own death used as counter-propaganda? Of a man who saved so many others yet couldn't save himself?

James F. Fixx was a brilliant publicist though an indifferent runner. He was primarily a writer, one who took to running and made his name and fortune that way. His *Complete Book of*

Running was read by millions, most of whom were inspired to rush out of doors immediately to do their first run. Jim was probably the man most responsible for the Great American Running Boom, a boom that is still going today and ten years on shows no signs of dying out.

But Jim's own sad and sudden death from a heart attack while out jogging was responsible for frightening off millions more potential runners. The anti-running lobby had a field day. They made sure that Jim became even more famous by his death than by his life. 'King of Jogging dies while out jogging,' they rejoiced.

Such opposition is largely made up of no-hopers: people governed by inertia and envy, who can't summon up the energy to go exercising themselves, and don't see why anyone else should. They put forward no alternative system of their own for staying younger longer – if you gotta go, they sigh, you gotta go. At a pinch they may suggest changing down to low-tar cigarettes.

It made no impression on them to say that Jim had always had a heart problem or to point out that for every heart attack on the running trail there are a thousand thousand indoors – massive coronaries at office desks, in rocking chairs, or in bed. Would you recommend sedentary people not to go to work, or never to dare nod off to sleep?

What's far more important to note is that many, many thousands who die from heart disease could have been saved by regular exercise. The statistics are firmly on our side. The incidence of heart disease in the USA has dropped during the past decade just as the running craze got going – and at last there is scientific research which links the two.

In fact Jim Fixx himself would probably not have lived so long *but* for his running. His father died of a coronary at 43, Jim outlived him by nine years!

My own research offers the same conclusion. Each year I note the deaths of friends in the obituary columns (by the time you pass 60 death notices are of more interest then marriages and births). I note with sadness the deaths of non-runners, often younger than me who have died of heart attacks, lung cancer, bronchial complaints. The runners, on the other hand, go on well into their 70s, 80s, and beyond; only then do they fade away. No one claims that running will give you a guarantee of eternal life. I used to wonder nevertheless about old Duncan Maclean, the 'Tartan Flash', whether he wouldn't still be with us to see in Eternity. At 92 he was still racing and generally full of beans. It was then that his doctor advised him, for health reasons, to pack it up. I went to visit him on his 93rd birthday, because I'd heard he wasn't feeling so well. When I called his wife Elsie, a mere spring chicken of 70, announced me, and Duncan, as I've said earlier, did a little skip in the air where he stood and ran down the hall to shake my hand. 'Hoy, Sylvester!' I was sorry to hear less than a year later that we had lost him after all.

Hazard on the roads

The only real danger of running is an avoidable one – being knocked down by a motor vehicle.

To show how the anti-running lobby can distort the statistics to their advantage, I recall an issue of one of the British medical free sheets, which banner-headlined a story 'Jogging Can Kill'. I scrutinised this carefully, to find that its substance was a quotation from an imported 'scientific' source stating that 7,000 joggers had been killed on American roads in the previous year. That sounded an alarming figure. However, on following up the references buried in the text and digging a bit I discovered that in fact the quotation was from a handout of the American Automobile Association – 7,000 *pedestrians* had been killed by cars that year! It required some effort to get the doctors' free tabloid to print a small retraction later. They weren't as proud of this story as the sensational first instalment.

Nevertheless motor vehicles *can* kill! I have known personally three athletes who have been knocked down and killed while training on the roads and several more who were badly injured, including a most promising girl marathoner, who was never able to come back to the sport. I also know two runners badly hurt by cars while training on cycles to rest foot injuries.

So take *excessive* care when road racing or road running! Over and above the ordinary dangers of being a pedestrian the runner often behaves in a rather 'macho' way, thinking he is a remarkable performer to be admired by all who pass, especially motorists. He takes risks, cuts corners and heads into trouble. I say 'he' but there are women who act like this too. Runners also tend to forget that their judgment is impaired – while the body is going at twice the speed, the brain, when fatigue sets in, is acting at only half the speed.

On country roads, should you run on the right to face the oncoming traffic, or on the left, so that any vehicle which may hit you is going more slowly relative to yourself? This conundrum has been extensively debated. I believe you should run on the right and see the traffic approaching so that you can take evasive action. Do not *allow* a vehicle to hit you!

It's the same with pollution . . . . don't fight back, just keep out of its way. Where you have the choice, run away from cars, especially on those days when the air seems to smoke and fumes seem to hang in the air, and seek the pure oxygen in the country-side. What other advice could you expect – to run along with the head close to the ground, or wearing an oxygen mask?

As for ice, and the risk of a tumble, see Chapter 15 on clothing for snowy conditions. Dog-bite dangers, too, are dealt with else-where, in Chapter 19. Some other time we will come to devising some nasty hazards for the anti-running lobby.

Meanwhile here's a cautionary tale reported to me by Peter Harvey, Chairman of the Vets AC.

It shouldn't happen to a vet!

It was a dark and stormy night and the vets of Collingwood AC were out on a club training run along the busy Purley Way, Croydon, when Martin MacAndrew lost his front tooth with plate. Without it he was done for, couldn't even complete the run, it was so essential to his image. He'd found it often enough before, down the kitchen sink, under the wardrobe. But this time it had rolled along the pavement and down the drain.

Martin yelled to the man in front, big Frank Prosser, who stayed back to help. They lifted up the grating and there was the tooth, just out of reach. So with Frank holding on to his legs, Martin gingerly lowered himself head-first into the drain. At this moment, a car driving past, thinking there had been an accident, braked to a halt alongside. Now there *was* an accident: the next car behind bashed into him, and a third car coming along the Purley Way went into the two of them.

Not knowing all this, two other vets, Rob Wilson and Peter Harvey, were sprinting up behind, panting excitedly, looking for help to deal with a youngster at the last alleyway who'd cornered a girl and was threatening her with a knife.

Then, finally, an off duty policeman who happened to be driving past spotted the accident. As he got out of his car, up came Rob with the other urgent appeal. The policeman stood there, perplexed to know which way his duty lay, while Rob and Peter were doing all they could to recover their breath. By which time Martin, tooth back in place, blissfully unaware of all this kerfuffle, sailed on with Frank to complete his evening's mileage.

No wonder there's a growing movement against running . . . . it would be safer, say some, simply to take the dog for a walk.

15 WEAR AND GEAR

Running is for all classes, all types, all ages and all schools of style. When it comes to dressing for it, the choice of gear on offer is as wide as you fancy.

As long as you take care of function, you can thus go wild on fashion. You can wander as far as you like along that road, answering the demands of fun, trendy design, team publicity or gadget fantasy. Or you can stop short at the basic outfit.

Either way, whatever you wear will be seen as an extension of your character. A dour, no-fuss person will go out in a ghastly, faded running vest, used ever since he first took up the sport 25 years ago. It's nothing but his own personal fashion display, of course, advertising the fact that he's a tough old dog, yer know, leader of the pack and all that.

At the other end there's the outgoing sort, not very sure of her prowess, hiding behind a smart and noisy two-tone track suit, rather stunning. And why not, let's deck ourselves out . . . . have fun!

Whichever style you adopt, it won't make a hundredth of a second's difference to your performance. No, I'm wrong, quite wrong, perhaps the clothes that proclaim to the public 'I am a Runner' will give that beginner a bit of extra confidence – and a dose of confidence is ever worth a yard or two.

But there are two important items of gear that certainly play their part in helping you to best times and distances and keeping you safer from injury: both Honest Ed and Flash Flossie's performances benefit from the right footwear and the right warm wrappings for the body.

If you want to get to the top, start at the bottom – with your feet and their shoes. Running is a cheap sport, you don't pay out on expensive equipment, large membership fees, hiring a boat or a court . . . . so it's worth while coddling your feet by spending on your shoes. It will be a major investment.

No, don't simply assume that tennis shoes, plimsolls or any old flats will answer the purpose, while demonstrating to the world that you're the sort of relaxed person that doesn't have to care all that much. You need specialised shoes for your chosen sport. (Of course if you really are tough and very experienced it could be a different matter. I have only to think of my friend Ron Hopcroft, who does insist on his old plimsolls. When you have behind you his thousands of miles of world-class running, maybe you can graduate to such fearlessness, too. Ron, by the way, just after the war, held the Bath to London running record).

So decide on a pair of specialised shoes, and buy them at a specialist shoe shop – not at a chain shoeshop, but a shop entirely devoted to equipping runners. This will be staffed by runners, no doubt, who know the sport quite as well as they know their merchandise. I once took part in the Burnham Beeches half-marathon in company with eleven members of the staff of the Cobra shoeshop. All but one finished ahead of me – they knew their stuff!

These sort of people look after the most elite of runners and will yet answer the daftest of your own questions. To track down such a shop near your home the best plan is to look in the directory near the back of *Running* Magazine. A good bit of my advice on gear has been culled from the magazine, which like these shops caters for both beginner and champion.

Shoes

When you go to one of these shops, be prepared to spend some time there – not to nip in and out with your purchase in less than five minutes. Avoid the type of shop where the shoes are displayed on shoe trees and stuffed with newspaper. They're not greengrocery – you should be able to pick them up, feel inside them, bend them, examine them.

Don't go with fixed ideas. What the next person is wearing may not be the shoe for you. A while back, one particular shoe became very popular as a 'cult' shoe because people liked the look of it – but it was a totally unsuitable shoe for the heavier beginner. And don't look at the news pictures of big marathons and go for the same shoes as the winner – these are lightweight racers for fast runners and rather than set you on course for a 2:07 marathon they may well cause you injury as they don't have the vital support and shock absorption that you need.

Be prepared to spend around £20 on your first pair of shoes, if not more. Try on all the shoes you can afford – and a few you can't. If your feet can tell the difference between the £20 and £30 shoe it'll be worth shelling out a bit more – if not, you've got a bargain.

Test Drive

Go in the socks you will wear for running (or buy your first pair in the shop) and try them on with the shoes. Try on different models of shoe and take advantage if the shop's policy is to allow you a 'test drive' in the street. After all, you are going to run on pavement and hard ground in the shoes, not stand around on fitted carpets (except in the pub afterwards).

The size of your ordinary walking shoe is only a rough guide to the size of running shoe you will need. For one thing, you may well need a shoe that is a half or even a whole size larger than your normal shoes. For another, US and continental sizings don't always align exactly with UK sizings. The most important thing is that the shoe fits your foot at its widest. That's why it's often a good idea to buy in the afternoon when your feet have warmed up and expanded. Try a variety of sizes and widths (if available). A general rule of thumb is that you should allow about ½″ between your big toe and the toe box and that your foot should not overhang the base of the shoe and bulge into the uppers. However, while there is plenty of room for your toes to move, there should be no such margin for your heels which should fit snugly with no sideways movement.

Don't imagine that, like leather shoes, your running shoes can be 'broken in'. *If they don't fit in the shop, they'll never fit.*

Shock absorption

The two properties that set a running shoe apart from any other sports or walking shoe are shock absorption and support. Each foot hits the ground approximately 800 times per mile – about 60 tons per foot per mile for a 10 stone runner. And your running surface may not always be level – there will be cobbles, and bumps, and cracks in the pavement and rocks and unevenness on your more rural runs. So you need some material between your foot and the ground which will absorb this shock. With this in view look for the midsole – your main shock absorber. The most commonly used midsole material is a polymer called EVA (Ethylene Vinyl Acetate) into which bubbles of air have been passed in different amounts. The more bubbles, the lighter and springier the midsole; the fewer, the more supportive. Like Goldilocks and the porridge, shoe boffins have been researching for many years to get a midsole consistency with just the right balance of sponginess, support and flexibility. Often the midsole will have two densities of EVA – with the firmer piece under the heel and the lighter, more flexible density under the ball of the foot.

Many midsole extras are available which offer extra shock absorption such as a small inflated cushion under the heel. You needn't worry too much about extras at this stage: certainly you shouldn't buy a shoe that has them if it's not comfortable!

The other major purpose the running shoe serves is support. The *heel counter* is a cup made either of plastic or reinforced board which wraps round the back of the shoe. Sometimes heel counters are 'extended' or 'reinforced' for additional support – though again, these are sophistications you don't have to worry about immediately. What is important is that your heel fits snugly into the shoe without any sideways movement.

Your choice of *outsole* really depends on the expected use of the shoe. If you live in an area where most of your running is on pavement or road, you may prefer a flat, wavy profile of sole which gives good traction on pavements and absorbs shock by being soft and springy. If, on the other hand, most of your running is likely to be done in country areas on uneven terrain, then you'll want a studded or waffle shoe. These are usually made of a tougher, carbonised rubber. The studs act as mini-shock-absorbers, so many studded shoes are also suitable for road use.

Inside the shoe you should find no rough edges or seams which could cause you blisters. The *insock* smooths away some of the differences between the shape of your foot and the shape of your shoe, and many are now made of 'memory' foam that moulds to your foot's shape. But there are still a lot of gaps between shoe and foot, and though many runners get by without socks, most of us need to avoid the friction that builds up and causes blisters. There are a number of specialist running socks on the market, though you can get by with a chain store sports sock if it doesn't have awkward seams across the toenails. You might have shied away from man-made fibres thinking that they would be hotter and more uncomfortable, but in fact recent developments mean that the synthetics are often a better buy, being cooler, more absorbent, cheaper and longer-lasting than cotton or wool.

For women, the choice of serious running shoes is gradually expanding. There was a time not too long ago when the only concession made to women runners was to make cheap trainers in pink – fine for lazing round in, but not built for serious running. Fortunately that's changing – a good thing, because there *is* a difference. A woman's foot tends to be narrower at the heel and instep, and a slightly different shape, though her toes spread out just as much at the front of the shoe. A standard shoe may fit a woman at the front but not be supportive enough at the heel. Try on all the fittings available to you – standard and women's – there's nothing to stop a man wearing a women's shoe if it's more supportive! Some women's shoes are still pink and feminine and there's no doubt that they look nice – but remember that there's nothing feminine about mud!

Basic Clothing

That's your feet covered. Now you can look at the clothes. At first, you don't have to think too hard or shell out too much. Any loose-fitting casual clothes you already have lurking in the depths of the wardrobe will do – T-shirts, jeans with sagging waistbands, slacks, woollen jerseys. But ultimately you'll find that feeling good will make you want to look good, too, and in a few weeks you'll be back at the shop buying some smart clothes.

First, though, underwear. For both men and women the best bet is snug-fitting cotton briefs providing support for men and absorbency for women. Some shorts for men and women have built-in pants but these aren't always as comfortable, as they may be made of the same non-stretch material as the shorts, or the material may be uncomfortable if worn close to the skin.

Lucky the flat-chested woman who doesn't knock herself out at every stride, and can run bra-less. But most aren't so well catered for. Sad to say, you won't find sports bras in all running shops yet and it may mean a trek to a big store with a corsetry department. These tend to be a bit frumpy, but you can be assured of coming away with a bra that fits. Look out for Triumph, Warner and Berlei sports models.

Again, when it comes to vests, the new synthetics may surprise you. If you prefer cotton you'll find that, though cool, if it gets waterlogged with perspiration or rain it will stay that way, while nylon tricot is a knitted material which wicks water away from the skin – to keep you cool if it's hot, warm if it's not. Look out for well-finished seams and armholes that are not too tight.

Freedom shorts – nylon tricot with a built-in brief – are becoming very popular with women and men as they are modest but free-moving. In general, women are still wearing the older style towelling knicker-type shorts on the track and in cross-country, but newer runners tend to feel over-exposed in these when road running. Shorts are another thing, like shoes, that you should try on carefully. If the outside looks big enough, the inner pant, if there is one, may not be. Raise your leg so that your thigh is parallel with the floor. If the shorts are not comfortable over the widest range of movements, buy the next size up. Your stride may be no more than a shuffle now, but you don't want to feel that your legs are tied together when you start getting faster.

Tracksuits come in all shapes and sizes and materials. You need to decide, primarily, what you want a tracksuit for. Is it for warming up and down in and taking off while you are running? Or for running in all the time in the winter? Or for changing into to look good après-run? You've such a wide choice now. Fleecy-lined cotton 'sweats' are cheap, absorbent and comfortable, and now come in all sorts of nice fashionable colours – but they can leave you very soggy in a downpour. Cotton/synthetic mixes keep their shape better after washing.

If you are choosing a 'functional' tracksuit rather than a good-looking one, the trousers should have tapered legs – not straight or flared – and long zips so that you can get them on and off over shoes. It's nice if there is a secure pocket for money or keys. Look for a top that is not too long or too tight at the waist, or it may part company with the trousers, leaving your midriff exposed. If you have a lot of sweat tops you might just want one pair of trousers, and, if it is possible, buy tracksuit trousers separately and cheaply. The lighter weight ones are called 'tracksters'.

Tracksuit wear fulfils its most important practical function in bad weather – wet or cold, or both – and judging by past performance we'll be getting quite a bit of that in Britain during these next few years. There are two things to be said about running in unpleasant conditions, at first seemingly contradictory – ignore the cold and rain, and carefully protect yourself from it. The point here is that you should never let the conditions stop you going out. Once you're warm it's as much a joy to run a freezing trail as a dry and sunny one. So make sure to start off warm; this can be achieved very simply by putting on extra layers, as many as you please, you could need three running vests on top of one another, and then the tracksuit. If rain is around add a wet suit on top of all the rest. This will ensure that you step out of the front door with a smile on your face.

Many people don't take any precaution at all if it's warm and there's only rain to be feared. Said the great champion Mike Gratton once: 'I run in the rain in just T-shirt and shorts if not too cold. I like to get away with as little as possible – once you are wet you are wet – a T-shirt doesn't get too heavy and is therefore better than trudging around in a top which has stretched to your knees, or tracksuit bottoms which have become so wet and heavy that they keep falling down.'

Snow provides a marvellous environment for a run. You need your many layers then plus thick gloves, for it's the extremities that require special care. You may also need shoes adapted to the terrain, to keep you safe; flat road trainers, ideal for dry weather, will not grip on snow and ice or wet grass. Some sort of ripple/stud/waffle sole is the answer, the equivalent of the motorist's chains.

The good shoe-shops keep up with the latest models turned out by the manufacturers, so you can hunt around for just the right bad-weather, bad-terrain training shoe or racer. We're mostly discussing cross-country running in this context. Racers, as any dedicated cross-country runner will tell you, are hard to find these days. The reason is that when the roadrunning boom began the shoe companies switched their interest from the traditional cross-country runners to the mass market. There are indications that new runners are turning to cross-country and not surprisingly the shoe-men are following.

Cross-country shoes fall into three broad categories:

Spikes: suitable for racing on courses without stretches of road.

Racers: Without spikes and so suitable for racing on mixed road/country courses, but without enough cushioning for training.

Road/trails trainers: With a sole suitable for training both on the road and on reasonably firm grassland.

For either training or racing purposes look for a ridged or studded shoe but with studs far enough apart so that the sole will not pick up excessive mud.

The remaining one of your extremities needs its own particular protection, too, in dirty weather – the head will benefit from a hat or balaclava. We're often warned of the large amounts of heat lost through the head; keeping it warm has the effect of keeping the body itself warm.

The normal wet-suit, very considerately, provides a dry housing for the head as well as the body. In choosing a wet-suit you will most probably go for nylon, which is cheap. Nylon rainsuits are no more than adequate; Gore-tex suits keep you far drier and are a marvellous luxury, but are correspondingly more expensive. Gore-tex is the market-leader in 'breathable' materials. What's special about it is that each square inch of its inner membrane contains some nine billion pores – I take the manufacturer's word for it, I've not sat down and counted – each of which is large enough to allow molecules of water vapour produced by perspiration to escape, yet too small to allow droplets of water to penetrate.

According to research, white or light-coloured clothing is not good enough if you want to avoid being involved in a road accident while you are out clocking up your winter training miles. A 'token' reflective sash worn over dark clothing is not much good, either. The best method to be seen at night is to complement light clothing with some *reflective* (a key word; 'fluorescent' colours are not the same, nor as effective) bands and stickers fixed to your arms and legs, or use something like the 'Glowdisc'. These devices help to make you more visible because their constant movement attracts the attention of drivers in the distance.

For the same reason, if you wear gloves in colder weather, wear white ones. Like a policeman on traffic duty, they will help you to indicate your intentions clearly to other road users.

Perhaps you could also consider wearing lights as cyclists are obliged by law to do. Obviously bike lamps are too heavy for runners, but there are some lightweight lights which could be fixed to a belt or jacket – just ensure that when adopting such a precaution, you follow it through completely and have a white light to your front and a red light behind you.

Gadgets and Gimmicks

You're now well shod, well-warmed and safe. Your remaining budget can go on aids, accessories and novelties.

The stop watch This is the main running aid. It's not necessary to run by the watch, but in your early days it helps you keep to a steady schedule and ensure that you don't run for longer than you should. And it's useful to time yourself over a favourite distance at least once a week as a measure of progress.

The wrist watch that doubles as a stop watch is these days almost indispensable for road runners. Even on the track in an important race you may see half the competitors pressing the start button when the gun goes and the stop button when they go through the finish line. Probably in the mere doing of it they lose a hundredth of a second, for its requires an awkward movement. You may use Mickey Mouse affairs costing as little as £5, or you can go to far more ambitious heights. A good quartz digital with a stainless steel strap, timing to $\frac{1}{100}$ second and all the usual features – date, alarm and so on – should be under £20.

Hand-held watches are more serviceable for high-speed operation and for timing two or three or more finishers together when you are acting as a spectator, coach or official. Some people are known to go to a three-figure sum for a sophisticated and highly accurate job.

150

Pulse meters A convenient type for runners who watch their pulse beat carefully is the Actimeter which takes the pulse at the fingertips. It is attached to the wrist and shows heart rate per minute. You set maximum and minimum pulse levels and a bleep tells you if you trespass over the limit. It measures $90 \times 43 \times 16$mm, not quite as compact as a watch. The digits are easy to read.

Anti-mugging alarm This emits a horrific shrill scream when the top is pressed down, enough to scare off an attacker and summon help. It's the size of a lipstick; a holder is available for carrying round the neck.

The *EPC 2000* home fitness computer designed to measure blood pressure and pulse rate. Roughly the size of a paperback book, it incorporates a pre-formed cuff which slips over the upper forearm. Oscillations in the artery walls are measured every 200 milliseconds by using high speed, high resolution pressure sensors. These readings are then converted via the micro-computer to liquid crystal display.

The *Heating Pad* from *Dreamland* (the world's largest manufacturer of electric underblankets) is a small, flexible, electrically-heated pad which can be wrapped round limb or torso.

For Injuries

Energy-Pak Magnetic Foil, designed for treating minor sports injuries. The foil application is based on the idea that electromagnetic energy fields can do good in body healing, because this type of energy can be correlated to similar natural forces in the body. The application of a magnetic field increases the flow of blood to the area being treated and so simultaneously increases the removal of waste products and the oxygen supply to the area.

Foot massage

Deep and relaxing foot massage – without taking your shoes off. That's the claim of the *Massator Pedio*, a West German-made machine which simulates manual massage of the feet. Five minutes' machine massage is said to be equivalent to 30 minutes' manual massage. It can also be used, at different angles, for calf and back massage and can be programmed to massage the reflex zones of the feet.

Footcare

Athlete's Foot Gel from *Scholl* is a new formulation which can help soothe and eventually eradicate the itchy discomfort of athletes foot-suffered by athletes and non-athletes alike. The colourless, odourless gel is easy to apply and doesn't need to be dressed.

The *Toshiba Vibratone* is a battery-operated home massager which can be applied to neck, shoulder, lower back or wrapped around calves or thighs (fastening with Velcro).

Dry hi-fi

Sony's all-weather *Walkman* is rain-resistant and designed to operate if accidentally dropped into water. (The earphones are water-resistant, too). The Walkman is a cassette player and FM radio combined, and has an anti-rolling system so that the tape doesn't jump while you're on the run.

Computer software

Jogger is a game for the Sinclair ZX Spectrum personal computer. The joggers in it are pretty manic, though. How many people do you know whose normal route involves fording a river full of boats and alligators, and crossing the motorway? The aim is to get three joggers across safely. When you reach a higher level of competence the whole thing speeds up, you have more joggers to play with, and worse, your jogger has to negotiate rampaging lawnmowers on the central reservation.

A more serious application for the ZX Spectrum is the *Jogger's Diary*. If you're a 'chartist' – one who likes to go back over favourite routes charting your progress – then this is ideal for you. You can feed in and store dates, routes, times and descriptions of your runs. Then you can analyse your performance by route, ask for a bar graph of your weekly mileage, or ask for a list of all your runs over a certain period of time. Wisely, the package makes no claims to predict your performance in any event.

Lace weights

This is a product for those runners who have the Zatopek mentality and always want to make every training run that much more difficult.

Lace weights consist of two sets of canvas-type bags which are threaded onto your running shoe laces, with a velcro strap around the heel to hold the weights snugly in place. This avoids the uncomfortable rubbing that ankle weight users have encountered. Eight half-pound weight bags are supplied, and the instruction leaflet suggests using two of these bags on each foot when starting to use the weights, thus providing a very convenient form of resistance training.

One pound fixed onto both feet turns what would otherwise be a steady run into a tough grind which can leave the legs feeling tired and stiff for a couple of days afterwards, so (as with any standard training programme) remember to start using lace weights gradually and cautiously. Ensure that you do not cause new imbalances in your running action, by using the weights only once or twice per week.

Computer Shoe

Micro ingenuity has gone a step further – you will soon be able to buy training shoes that will tell you how long and how far you've jogged, how many calories you've burned and how your performance compares with previous outings.

After a run in the Puma RS Computer Shoe (and Software Package) you connect it by cable to an office or home computer and the information held by the shoe's computer circuitry housed in the heel can be displayed on screen.

Another trainer, the Adidas Micropacer, has the processor built into the laces of the left shoe, and after a run, its information can be displayed on a digital LCD watch-set.

The running boom has produced other oddities too: jogging

purses, wrist wallets, weighted gloves, sweat-bands with head-lights, nose-gripping 'lung trainers', foot shock absorbers, body fat calipers, baby jogger prams, shoe repair glue, 'tune belts' to carry keys, wallets, stereos and money, 'doggie tapper' to defend oneself, jog-pedometers, running rods for muscle training . . . . and Stinky Pinky, which claims to eliminate foot odours overnight if left in the shoes.

Next they'll re-invent the velocipede, to provide you with a handy seat while running and room for stowing lots more gadgets.

16   RATING YOURSELF AS A RUNNER

Once you've become a practised runner, you start measuring your performance. At first, it's simply so that you can watch yourself improve.

Then, after a particularly good outing, something more stirs in you. Exactly how good might I become, you wonder – is there any reason why I shouldn't go on and on improving until . . . . until I become a record breaker? It may be only a rather esoteric record, the sort cricketers indulge in . . . . say, the fastest person in the world of exactly 43 years 11 months and slightly balding, over a downhill 4,200m course on a wet Thursday in East Humberside. But it's something!

Or in contrast you may have had your ego deflated and you're ready to settle for checking yourself against mere age averages. Either way, what you need is a yardstick. To keep tables of comparative performances pinned on the wall acts as a constant incentive and inspiration.

Much work has been done by the British Veterans Athletic Federation on establishing tables of standards for runners. A man from Watford, committee member Harvey Jaquest, produced on its behalf a set of standards for all ages, for all track and field disciplines. Now adopted as a guide for those wishing to enter big championships, it's not a statistical average nor is it officially binding, but it says in effect that if you can measure up to a particular level you can consider yourself good enough to compete with the best in your age category.

In drawing up his tables Jaquest used not only his own great experience stretching over a couple of decades but also the published work of track statisticians. These people regularly compile listings such as annual veteran rankings, veteran national records, veteran world age group records and – distinct from these, as you'll see below – veteran world *age* records. He also considered the depth of entry in a multitude of events, as well as the depth of finishing. He looked at the slowest plodders as well as the former Olympic stars. This is what he came up with, not records but reasonable levels of achievement.

Suggested veteran standards – men

	40-44	45-49	50-54	55-59	60-64	65-69	70+
100m	13.5	14.1	14.8	15.2	16.0	17.0	19.0
200m	27.5	28.5	30.0	31.7	33.3	35.5	37.5
400m	60.0	62.5	64.5	67.5	73.0	78.5	85.0
800m	2:22	2:28	2:32	2:37.5	2:48	3:00	3:15
1,500m	5:00	5:15	5:30	5:47	6:03	6:20	6:55
5,000m	18:30	19:30	20:55	22:15	24:00	26:00	30:00
10,000m	41:00	43:00	47:00	49:00	53:00	56:50	60:00

Suggested veteran standards – women

	35-39	40-44	45-49	50-54	55-59	60-64	65-69
100m	15.5	16.5	17.5	18.5	19.5	20.5	21.0
200m	31.0	33.0	35.5	37.5	39.5	41.5	44.0
400m	74.0	82.0	92.0	104.0	114.0	125.0	140.0
800m	2:42	2:50	3:00	3:25	3:35	3:50	4:15
1,500m	5:40	6:00	6:30	6:50	7:25	7:55	8:30
5,000m	20:50	22:05	23:55	25:20	28:20	29:35	31:35
10,000m	45:00	49:10	52:50	55:40	60:40	64:10	68:10

(If you don't have a valid mark for your performances over these metric distances, but only for mile or 2 mile or 5-mile races, you can identify your place on the table with a bit of shrewd interpolation).

What is missing from these tables, of course, is the marathon. Marathon statistics are no exact science, after all, since courses vary so greatly (so do measuring standards!) thus we need to turn to other rankings to help us there.

Below is a bar graph, borrowed from American sources, of actual marathon best performances from the age of five up to eighty, for both men and women, recorded at five-year intervals. Don't read them as record marks, however, but more as a general indication of how you shape against the best and how each age group compares to those neighbouring it. (It's interesting to note that some American 5-year-old managed a marathon in about the same time as a woman of 75!)

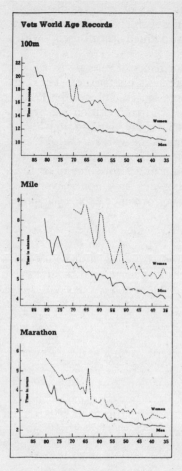

Vets World Age Records

100m

Mile

Marathon

Even the four-minute mile still remains unconquered by a vet, although there are many distinguished vet runners competing today who did get below the barrier ten or 15 years ago. The mile vet record stood at 4:12.5 in 1985 (by Bill Stewart of Ann Arbor, USA). Where is the Bannister of today who can knock off those last 12 seconds?

Veteran men of 40-49 get entry to the London Marathon by right if they have beaten 3 hrs; vets of 50-59, 3:20; women of 40-49, 3:20. A woman under 40 qualifies if she has been under 3:10. Older vets, men and women, are individually scrutinised – with a very generous eye.

The continuous variation in performance of veterans by age can be followed in more detail in my next set of statistics. These are graphs plotted from sets of world age-record tables of the 1980s.

Here the five-year groupings used in competition are broken down into year-by-year figures, so that if say you do 2:16 when 46 years old, you are still the fastest man in the world *at that age*, even if some comparative youngster of 45 has notched up a mark a few seconds faster. These are consolation prizes for some of us to be aiming at when the very greatest honours have gone beyond our reach. There is a slower decline in performance by age the longer the race.

In events other than the marathon the men's 40-year age record is of the order of 10 per cent slower than the open record. In the marathon age counts less – no doubt the aging runner has well-developed characteristics of stamina and pace judgement and so on to draw on; whereas in the middle-distance and sprint events these qualities are not enough to compensate for the loss of springiness and strength.

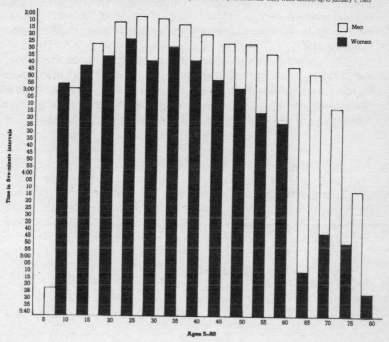

Marathon records by age

These are US records taken at ages five, 10 and so on up to 80 in five-year intervals. They were correct up to January 1, 1983

There is yet another useful set of veteran marathon standards to measure yourself against, that drawn up by the London Marathon. Note that this is essentially an elite standard, for the London's need is to allow automatic entry only to the topmost segment of marathoners in each age group – those who cannot produce proof of a high quality recent performance must take their chance in the general entry ballot.

You can read across horizontally from the tables to note for instance that the 100m time for a woman vet of 35 is roughly equal to that of a man of 54. You can also do the same sort of extrapolation for yourself – where would your mile time of 5.38 show up in the age table? Answer, it's about as good as that of the best 68-year-old man or 48-year-old woman, in the world. Keep going, undismayed!

Still on the age theme, the following tables give the records of men veteran runners in Britain as drawn up in 1985. These are in official five-year age groupings. (As a reminder, competition is divided off into 5-year groups, to give the older runners a chance to compensate for that falling away of performance year by year.)

UK Veteran Age Group Records (Men)

100m	R. Taylor	10.9	1978
200m	R. Taylor	22.2	1975
400m	J. Dixon	49.7	1973
800m	R. Anderson	1:56.3	1977
1500mm	N. Fisher	3:56.6	1977
5000m	M. Turner	14:22.0	1980
10,000m	M. Freary	29:47.0	1978
45-49			
100m	C. Williams	11.1	1978
200m	C. Williams	22.8	1978
400m	J. Dixon	50.5	1977
800m	B. Bartholomew	1:58.9	1982
1500m	B. Bullen	4:03.3	1978
5,000m	J. Baldwin	14:57.3	1982
10,000m	M. Freary	30:56.9	1983
50-54			
100m	R. Taylor	11.5	1984
200m	R. Taylor	23.15	1985
400m	P. Higgins	52.28	1979
800m	D. Thomas	2:05.7	1981
1500m	L. O'Hara	4:15.27	1984
5,000m	J. Hogan	15:37.1	1983
10,000m	W. Stoddart	32:42.0	1981
55-59			
100m	S. Stein	12.2	1977
200m	S. Brookes	25.06	1983
400m	F. Higgins	54.84	1985
800m	H. Tempan	2:12.0	1981
1500m	H. Tempan	4:23.3	1981
5,000m	L. Forster	16:25.60	1985
10,000m	S. Charlton	34:44.4	1982

60-64

100m	C. Fairey	12.3	1978
200m	C. Fairey	26.5	1977
400m	G. Bridgeman	60.7	1985
800m	H. Tempan	2:15.2	1985
1500m	H. Tempan	4:36.04	1985
5,000m	H. Tempan	17:40.8	1985
10,000m	R. McMinnis	36:16.0	1975

65-69

100m	J. Williams	13.0	1975
200m	C. Fairey	27.48	1982
400m	L. Batt	65.4	1979
800m	E. O'Bree	2:25.95	1985
1500m	E. O'Bree	5:00.28	1985
5,000m	R. McMinnis	19:14.5	1981
10,000m	G. Porteous	38:39.2	1979

70-74

100m	L. Watson	14.4	1985
200m	S. McSweeney	30.0	1982
400m	S. Busby	69.93	1982
800m	L. Rolls	2:57.14	1985
1500m	J. Farrell	5:22.4	1979
5000m	J. Farrell	19:33.0	1979
10,000m	J. Farrell	42:32.8	1979

75-79

100m	N. Martin	15.6	1977
200m	A. Sutherland	35.2	1977
400m	R. Carlyon	85.2	1981
800m	R. White	3:26.1	1979
1500m	R. White	6:53.6	1979
5000m	C. Bendig	23:17.1	1981
10,000m	R. Wiseman	53:54.0	1978

80-89

100m	N. Martin	17.1	1981
200m	N. Martin	37.5	1981
800m	R. White	4:44.9	1985
1500m	R. White	9.27.7	1985

90+

100m	C. Speechley	28.5	1978
200m	C. Speechley	76.8	1979

Listing produced from David Burton's listing of 12.7.85 and revisions at 25.9.85

Jeremy Hemming

161

Now that you've had this chance to assess your own quality, ask yourself another question: Am I sure I'm in the right event? And then: Might I not be much higher up the rankings at some other distance? Here's how to find the answers.

First you must realise that during these years of marathon madness, we have all come to believe that there is no running other than marathoning. But there is and it might suit you to know if you're a slow marathoner, that inside you there may be a fast quarter-miler struggling to get out.

Your ability at any distance is natural and inborn, depending on many factors – your size, the length of your legs compared to the rest of you, the strength of your thigh muscles or your shoulder muscles, your body weight ratio, your oxygen processing capacity, your muscle fibre proportions and a thousand other physical characteristics, plus your powers of endurance and mental control.

You may not have been endowed with the right mix to destine you for victory in the long, long 26.2 miles but you might do well at the cross-country, the triatholon, the middle-distance, or the sprints.

Using the Hungarian Tables you can pinpoint your precise best event. Then you may be able to unscramble yourself from the wrong event and concentrate on the right one. The truth is that a great marathoner will never be the world's fastest sprinter, no matter how hard he trains, and vice-versa.

The *Hungarian Scoring Table for Track and Field Events* gives a scale of points for times over various distances, based on the analysis of large numbers of international performances over recent years.

You test yourself out over each of the relevant distances, then read off points from the table; find the highest points score you achieve and that will tell you your best event. It's as simple as that. You should try to make a proper timed attack on each distance. A track is best for this (though not essential) but if you're going to be very dedicated, the ideal thing is to enter a race. Look out for open or graded meetings – these cater for all standards and usually charge only a modest entry fee.

Of course, we're concentrating in the table on that part of the range that applies to the average veteran runner – and assuming that high-scoring, world class competitors already know their best distances!

Choosing your best distance

Men

Points	100m	200m	400m	800m	1,500m	Mile	5,000m	10,000m	Marathon
500	12.71	26.11	57.26	2:10.5	4:32.1	4:51.2	17:00.8	36.09.1	2:53:36
450	12.95	26.67	58.42	2:13.0	4:37.8	4:56.9	17:22.2	36:57.8	2:57.46
400	13.21	27.26	59.86	2:15.5	4:43.5	5:02.9	17:44.9	37:49.3	3:02:11
350	13.49	27.88	1:00.96	2:18.3	4:49.7	5:09.3	18:09.1	38:44.1	3:06:52
300	13.79	28.56	1:02.37	2:21.2	4:56.4	5:16.2	18:35.1	39:42.9	3:11:55
250	14.11	29.29	1:03.90	2:24.4	5:03.6	5.23.6	19:03.3	40:46.9	3:17:23
200	14.47	30.10	1:05.60	2:28.0	5:11.7	5:31.9	19:34.5	41:57.5	3:23:27
150	14.87	31.02	1:07.52	2:32.0	5:20.8	5:41.2	20:09.9	43:18.0	3:30:15
100	15·35	32.11	1:09.79	2:36.7	5:31.6	5:52.3	20:51.8	44:53.1	3:38:27
50	15.97	33.53	1:12.75	2:42.9	5:45.6	6:07.7	21:46.3	46:56.6	3:49:02
1	17.20	36.32	1:18.57	2:55.0	6:13.2	6:35.0	23:33.6	51:00.0	4:09:52

Women

Points	100m	200m	400m	800m	1,500m	3,000m	Marathon
500	14.60	31.07	1:08.03	2:40.0	5:13.3	11:57.9	3:44:41
450	14.93	31.89	1:09.67	2:44.1	5:20.3	12:16.4	3:51:37
400	15.28	32.75	1:11.40	2:48.4	5:27.7	12:36.1	3:58:57
350	15.65	33.67	1:13.24	2:53.1	5:35.6	12:56.9	4:06:45
300	16.04	34.66	1:15.22	2:58.0	5:44.0	13:19.3	4:15.07
250	16.47	35.73	1:17.37	3:03.4	5:53.2	13:43.7	4:24.14
200	16.95	36.91	1:19.75	3:09.4	6:03.4	14:10.7	4:34:18
150	17.49	38.26	1:22.45	3:16.1	6:15.0	14:41.2	4:45:43
100	18.13	39.85	1:25.65	3:24.1	6:28.6	15:17.4	4:59.15
50	18.96	41.92	1:29.80	3:34.5	6:46.4	16:04.5	5:16:50
1	20.60	46.00	1:37.98	3:55.0	7:21.4	17:32.2	5:51:28

Hungarian Athletic Association

To make it clear, let's take the typical example of Joe Jogger. He's good for a 3:33 marathon (211 points), and has managed 41:15.7 for a 10k road race on a very hot day (229 points). Now he gets himself down to a track on four evenings – separated by several weeks while he gets his body fitted out for shorter distances – and comes up with 19:10.5 for the 5,000m (238 points); 5:04.7 for the 1,500 (243 points); 2:26.8 for the 800 (216 points); 1:07.7 for the 400 (145 points); 32:49 for the 200 (85 points); and 15:49 for the 100m (87 points).

So Joe should have a serious go at the 1,500m where he clocked up most points. Over the months he can train specifically for this event and thus gradually improve his time and score. One historic day he might go out and break the 5 minute mile barrier. On the other hand, he might never get below 3 hours for a marathon, however hard he trains.

You don't have to try every event – and you'll have to make approximations from the chart – but it may be a start.

If you feel inspired to move down in distance or move over to the track, you should be able to find an ordinary athletic club in your neighbourhood, which will be glad to have you as a member. You might even get into their second string competition, but at any rate, you'll be able to attend their club training nights to pick up some coaching and advice.

Instead of a case history to illustrate the difference between runners at the extremes of the ability range – sprinters and long distance runners – here is a fable about two vets. We'll call one of them Charlie and one Samantha.

They train together at the track all week, at the end of the daily training session entering into a contest with each other. On Mondays, Wednesdays and Fridays, Charlie gives Samantha a 20-metre start and has to try to catch her. It's worth one point.

Bang! At the gun they set off and every single time Charlie overhauls her. Well, is it that she's 'only' a woman? Anyhow by the end of the week Charlie has this total score: 3.

Then on the Tuesdays, Thursdays and Saturdays, Samantha gives Charlie a 20-metre start and has to try to catch him.

Bang! They set off and every single time she catches him, no matter how he exerts himself. (He's only a man!) By the end of the week, her score: 3.

The secret's a simple one . . . . Charlie is a sprinter and can dash off fast, but like every sprinter he tires after a few hundred metres, while Samantha the stayer remorselessly stays on his tail and in due course, at about the half mile mark, overhauls him.

Find out if you're a Charlie or a Sam!

17   THE GREATEST

Each year the veteran movement produces its champion runners. There are champions for each age group from 35 and 40 right through to the 80s and even 90s. There are champions in each of these age groups for every *race*, from the 100m to the marathon and beyond. There are champions of the track and champions of the road and of the cross-country. There are champions of the World Vets official movement and of the old-established road running movement, IGAL, and of other minor movements, too. There are men champions and women champions.

Taken together you thus find there are well over 200 different Champions of the World. Who can we choose among them – which man and which woman – to nominate as Champion of Champions?

I decided to run my own little poll, to select the champion veterans of the 1980s.

In an attempt to narrow down the task I laid down a number of criteria. For a start I decided to restrict the possibilities to long-distance racing, in particular road-racing. After all that is where the bulk of the competition is, and the bulk of the interest among veterans generally.

I then decided that the award should be open – within the age limits of veterans. That is to say, the champion should be the fastest and best man or woman, at whatever age. Unfair on the Over 80s, Over 70s, and Over 60s and pretty well impossible in fact for all but the Over 40s and Over 45s and maybe Over 50s, but there again the great mass of membership and competition is in these younger age groups.

Then I threw in consistency as a requirement – I was not looking for a flash-in-the-pan winner in one event in one year, but someone with notable performances over a broad period.

After all this was done I still had a short list which was not at all *short*. I noted that the names listed derived from two different streams – the 'golden oldies', international champions in their youth, and the born-again or new-breed runners, who had only turned to the sport in their veteran years. But that wasn't to influence the decision.

So to whittle down the list still further, I had to inflict my own arbitrary choice on matters – giving points as it were for depth of competition, toughness of course and local conditions.

I then had the following final list of winners of important distance races over the past three or four years: Les Roberts, Gunter Mielke, Jim McNamara, Mike Turner, Barry Brown, Dave Clark, Tim Johnston, Taff Davies, Alan Rushmer, Guy Ogden, A. Villaneuva, Roger Robinson and Mike Connolly.

Among the women I eventually short-listed: Linda Findley, Ford Madeira, Priscilla Welch, Gabriela Andersen-Schiess, Joyce Smith, Bev Shingles and Leslie Watson (for amazing consistency). In fact it was because there was less consistency among the women, that it emerged as a shorter list.

I shuffled the names around, ran through in my mind again the races I'd seen, for finer points, studied the reports of races I'd missed and at last came out with my nominations. In both the divisions I found I had picked runners approaching the end of their fifth decade.

My Champion of Champions in the men's division was Taff Davies, of Aldershot, 48 in 1986, and Joyce Smith, also 48 in 1986.

Here are their short biographies:

Taff Davies – Sergeant Major Tecwyn Davies – had been winning veteran championships since he turned 40, in 1978. Year after year he has contested Southern England, British and world races, winning perhaps three-quarters of the events entered.

Probably his greatest triumph came in the world championship at Lytham St Annes, near Blackpool in 1985, where he won the 10,000m from Alan Rushmer, leaving the favourite Barry Brown, of the United States third, 8 seconds behind. Brown had been winning US national titles as well as a world event staged at San Diego earlier in the year, but they had never before competed head to head.

It is probably in that hard, head to head stuff that Davies makes his mark. The year before he had missed the British national veterans cross-country championship and Guy Ogden, just 40, took the title. In 1985 Davies was eager to be avenged; well, he did take back the title, when already 47 years old, but did not have the satisfaction of beating Ogden, who was absent due to injury.

Davies has been an athlete for thirty years, having kept going in the Army since leaving school. At Aldershot he had the frustrating record of having been six times runner up – in the army cross-country competition. But he never gave up trying. 'I was determined to win and it was that which kept me in the sport.' Finally he did win the army open title, at the age of 39.

That was an excellent send-off to veteran running. I remember him running through the woods in the Southern cross-country in his first year as a vet. I was in this race myself, striving not to be last of all, when he came charging through, a lap ahead of us back-markers, to sprint through the finish line, well ahead of the field.

He went on to win the national crown, which he held for many of the intervening years.

All that was done against a background of army service at home or abroad in Northern Ireland and Bahrain. There in Belfast, he found a way of keeping in shape, by running up and down the 3,220 steps of the Grand Central Hotel, road running not being permissible.

It was when he came out of regular barracks service that Taff Davies could finally devote himself to a more organised training programme and begin to build up the consistency and quality of his racing. He now does some 70 miles a week, two or three days in the week running both morning and evening. 'I go for quality rather than quantity,' he says of his training.

The one race he does not do is the marathon – he hasn't undertaken one in almost twenty years. He's a man tailored to the 10,000m.

To many British women, Joyce Smith is a symbol and a reminder of what women can do in the male-dominated world of running. Through her natural ability and rigorous training she has broken records and set a new standard for women runners.

Joyce has been an athlete all her life. She joined the Hampstead Harriers (later to amalgamate with Barnet and become the Barnet Ladies AC) at 17, as a sprinter and long-jumper – but she soon found out she wasn't either. She ran in an 880 yd race just for the points and broke the club record with a time of 2:31. Since that day she has been a middle-distance runner. At the age of 22, in 1960 she ran the 880m in 2:10.2, and qualified for the Olympic Games; in the same year she won the National Cross-country title for the second time. In 1972, she ran the 1,500m heats in the Munich Olympics, for and briefly held the record for that distance with 4:09.4. She was then 34 years old.

In 1974, at the Women's AAA Championships in London, she was the first British woman to run the 3,000m in under 9 minutes, and her time of 8:55.6 ranked her then as third in the world over that distance. In the same year she won a bronze medal in the European Games 3,000m. In 1978, at the age of 40, she was training for the European 3,000m when she broke a bone in her foot and was out of running for three months. Her husband Bryan – then a PE teacher and also her coach – suggested that she take up distance running as a way of building back up. In June 1979, with only eight months of training behind her, she ran in the Avon Marathon at Sandbach and won in 2:41.37. The prize included a trip to the first Avon International Race in Waldniel, which she won in 2:36.37. In 1979 she was once again a winner of the Women's National Cross-Country Championship, not to mention the winner of the Tokyo marathon in 2:38.

What makes her achievements the more remarkable is that Joyce was a working wife and mother while all this was taking place. Lisa was born in 1968, and Lia in 1976. She ran in the early months of both pregnancies, and three months after Lia was born she ran in the National Road Relays. She also has a part-time accounting job, and all her training had to be fitted in around her job and family. Bryan gave up his own career as a runner to coach her, and when the girls were small, they often spent coaching evenings playing near the Copthall track while Bryan put Joyce through her paces. Bryan has always taken care of the technical side of Joyce's running, keeping track of her mileage and its effect on her. On long Saturday morning runs, he can often be found riding beside her on his bike, offering encouragement and liquid refreshment. He runs himself with the Shaftesbury Harriers, and works as Sports Liaison Officer for the Copthall Stadium, Hendon, and Joyce will tell you that he's done more than his fair share of babysitting until now!

Since 1981 Joyce has had a few ups and downs: looking back, she feels it was due to tackling too many marathons each year, which slowed her down and led to injury. In March of 1981, she was first in the Gillette London Marathon (2:29.57), but she developed shin splints afterwards and did no more marathon running that year. In 1982, she ran the London Marathon (2:29.43), but due to a stress fracture in her pelvis, she was out of competition the remainder of 1982. In 1983, she did a string of marathons: The International Women's Osaka Race (8th in 2:40.01), the Rome marathon (2:38.04), the Avon-Los Angeles marathon (5th in 2:34.39), the World Championships in Helsinki (9th in 2:34.27), and the Chicago marathon (12th in 2:39.43). Apart from the Chicago marathon, she had been gaining speed, but 1984's results were uneven: Najoya International (6th in 2:38.55), the LA Olympics (in which she captained the British Women's team and ran the marathon in 2:32.48, to gain 11th place), the Avon-Paris marathon (8th in 2:37.16), and the New York marathon (16th in 2:46.17). In January of 1985, however, she cut her time at the Osaka race by almost 2 minutes to place 7th (in 2:38.09) and in June she was second in the Rio marathon in Brazil with 2:42.

There you are – finest Over 35 woman runner in the world without a doubt.

18   DISABILITY OVERCOME

A man with a pacemaker inside his chest in a shoulder-to-shoulder
battle down the finishing straight . . . . a totally blind sprinter
powering around the bend of the 200m in a world record bid . . . .
another sprinter in a wild dot-and-dash effort on one good and one
artificial leg.

Those are glimpses of some of the disabled athletes who compete today on level terms in world veteran championships. No
quarter asked for, no quarter given, they win their medals on
straight athletic merit. Their own victories over disability show
that the modern world has been justified in providing full opportunities to all classes and all minorities, to the old and the lame.

At one time doctors felt themselves well rewarded if they could
keep disabled patients alive and comfortable. But more recently
the disabled and handicapped themselves decided that this was not
enough, they wanted full and normal living. Soon they began to
force the issue. In sport, for instance – often a leader in social and
political action – they won the right to a range of organised
competitions.

Eventually for some even the disabled games movement proved
limiting; they began working for full equality, with the backing of
medical science. The man with the pacemaker, for instance, was a
guinea-pig in the testing of an adaptation that would not only
prevent his heartbeat from dropping too low, but would allow it to
rise far above the 100 per minute rate, so that he could drive
himself as hard as any other runner.

The logical end of scientific work to improve the quality of life of
the disabled can now be seen. Perhaps it is this that has caused a
gradual change in attitudes to the disabled, a change towards their
complete acceptance. Thus it happened in the case of . . . .

He had been blind for forty years, yet it was only in the last ten with these new attitudes in the air, that the realisation could finally come to him: 'Why shouldn't I too be able to fly through the air with the greatest of ease and the greatest of enjoyment?'

And why not? For how he could fly . . . . once he'd found a method to keep running straight and once there was a readiness to bend the rules to admit him into normal competition. In fact, learning again to race for the first time since his teens, he became the fastest 60-year-old in all the world. The blind man was king!

Assmy, a West German, lost his sight in a plane crash in 1938, then 23. He was a runner as a young man, one of those lightly-built sprinters whose leg-speed is everything. But his face had to be rebuilt by plastic surgery after the crash and with it went his sight; running was no longer possible. Or so it seemed – until in the 1970s he was inspired by hearing of the exploits of other runners of his own age. Finally his son, a fair club athlete, persuaded him onto a track and they practised together, Fritz speeding along beside him connected by a short wrist tether.

Fritz prepared for his debut at world level at the 1977 veteran international at Gothenburg, Sweden. We in the British team had already heard of his abilities, but were backing Colin Fairey of Kettering against him for the Over 60 contest. In contrast to Assmy, Fairey was a big powerful runner, and the British record holder. He had been disappointed to miss the previous world event, and reckoned this to be his chance, but the week before the race he had allowed himself to dash impetuously after a youngster back at his home club for a bit of fun, without the precaution of warming up. A hamstring pull was the result.

Colin worked on the muscle assiduously, but as the meeting continued it steadily worsened. Because of his great talent he was able to progress, limping a bit, from heats to semi-finals to finals, but in the end he broke down yards from the tape. Assmy won of course, but the argument of who was the fastest man was not settled.

Assmy certainly beat the rest of the field, to great acclamation. His only defeat in the decade since those races was, very narrowly, against the great American ex-Olympian, Payton Jordan, at Puerto

Rico, 1983, in the 100m final. But he reversed this defeat in the 200m two days later and beat Jordan again in the 400m. Jordan, track runner and coach, said of him: 'He is truly a great sportsman, and to be blind, and accomplish what he has done, is phenomenal.'

A special ruling allows Assmy and son to run in the outside lane so that he does not obstruct other runners; and to run fairly, the son makes sure that he runs parallel with, not in front of his father. But there is still controversy about 'towing' – critics say that Assmy is being aided by a younger, stronger runner, and that, to be strictly fair, he should be accompanied by a runner in the same five-year age-group. But *who* could match him? As Assmy himself explains: The accompanist would have to run 100m in less than 12 seconds, 200m in less than 26, and 400m in less than 60. Only if he is fast enough and can run next to me without effort does he not hinder me . . . . If he could do those times he would well enter the race himself, if he were in the same age-group. No one is willing to do that.' He also explains how difficult it is to run attached to another by rope. His son has to arrange the starting blocks and put his father in the exact position so that he can run straight along his lane, and shout 'curve' before and during the track bends. Then he must yell 'straight' as they leave the curve, and call out the distance to the final several times. Fritz cannot lunge at the finishing tape the way other runners do – if he did, he would fall over. 'I do not know if you can imagine how strenuous and difficult it is,' he says, 'to run together on one lane of a track when one of the runners cannot see.' If he hadn't been so well grounded in athletics in his youth, he doubts whether he could run at all now. His advocates – and I am one – believe that he could run even faster if he could see. For one thing, he wouldn't have the extra burden of having to synchronise his stride and arm-swing with a companion. To see his run is to be inspired, and to realise just what the human body and brain can do together when motivated. Fritz Assmy has probably done more for the vets movement through his courage and determination than any other man.

Hip Replacement

Today a number of veterans are learning how the hip replacement operation may be treated as just a passing setback.

John Disley

On Christmas Eve, 1983, minutes before the traditional Ranelagh Harriers run, a clubmate told John Disley, aged 54, how well he looked – and John knew he was doomed. To his mind, looking well meant he hadn't been training hard enough, and he took it as a bad omen. He felt fine – apart from a nagging pain in his left leg that had bothered him for four years. It was being treated as sciatica, without much success. He was still able to run, although his leg seemed to hold him back slightly. In that race he hit rock bottom – only half-way round the 7-mile course, his left leg stiffened into a dead weight, and he barely managed to limp to the finish. The following 48 hours of pain drove him to a specialist. Before the doctor deadened the pain with an injection, he examined John carefully. He watched John's eyes as he performed a series of movements and announced: 'It's not your leg that's bothering you, old chap, it's your hip.' An X-ray confirmed a misalignment of the femur, and John was told he needed a hip replacement operation.

John Disley is a past Vice-Chairman of the Sports Council, 1952 Olympic bronze medallist in the steeplechase and now Course Director of the London Marathon. What had caused his hip to go? Had running aggravated it? 'Probably,' John says. 'If I hadn't done all that running it may never have come to light – but then I would have died believing I was perfect!'

In September 1984, John entered Charing Cross Hospital for the operation. He describes what they did: 'After making an incision, the doctors took out the top five inches of my left femur (containing the ball and bend) and bored a hole down into the remaining femur. A shaft of stainless steel shaped like the piece removed was then cemented into the femur, and the whole shaft mounted in a plastic socket which attached to the side of the pelvis. Then the muscles were stitched and the wound closed.' The following day the doctors had him up and walking; by day eight he was up and down the nine floors of the hospital with only one stick.

He was then allowed home and three weeks later he was cycling and running the length of Waterloo station for his train. By week thirteen he was back in action in one of his favourite haunts – 3,000 ft up Bow Fell in the Lake District!

John wasn't sure what his recovery would be like, so through *Athletics Weekly* he appealed for other runners with hip replacements to share their experiences. He received some interesting replies. One was from John Jackson the director of Plas-y-Brenin National Mountaineering Centre in North Wales, who was skiing ten weeks after the operation (and skiing much more smoothly his friends said). Another was from Alan Brent, who had been fitted with a new hip in early June and spent the summer building up the muscle tone in his leg on a variety of exercise machines. Five weeks later, he was running up and down the football pitch as a referee!

While these men were setting their own feverish pace of recovery, replies came from other runners who were taking it more easily, averaging eighteen months for their return to running. However, once they were back in action, many were taking on marathons as well as fell-running. John is a great believer in not pushing yourself too hard: 'Don't forget,' he says, 'that the whole process of discovery, diagnosis, operation and recovery may take up to three years, and you aren't going to run the same as when you were three years younger.'

John took things easy over a slippery winter, and is now running two or three times a week on soft ground. His only problem is that his right hip is starting to show the same symptoms as the other. It may be that he will need a second operation, but he is not worried about it, and feels confident that he can run with two new hips as well as with one.

For anyone in need of the operation he has no hesitation in recommending it. 'The pain doesn't go away or get any better,' he says, 'and prolonging the inevitable just makes the road to recovery that much longer.' There is normally a long waiting list, but John says that if you can convince the hospital you are willing to come in at a moment's notice, the wait can be reduced to weeks.

John's advice about recovery is to avoid jolting downhill runs, which may actually damage the cement content in the femur, and to replace running shoes every 1,000 miles so that the midsoles stay springy and shock-absorbent.

174

In November, 1984, Joan Glass then 45, a fell-runner in her native Wales, was also faced with the prospect of a hip replacement operation. Since 1977, she had competed regularly in the Welsh 1,000m and the Snowdon races. She had been a hill-walker since she was young; fell-racing just seemed a natural progression, especially as most of the races took place on her doorstep (Joan and her husband ran a youth hostel in Llanberis). When she was 14, however, doctors diagnosed osteomyelitis in the right hip, an inflammation in the joint caused by a knock or a virus. Joan took up fell-running without worrying because the occasional pain she suffered seemed unconnected with exercise and never lasted long. She would make the odd note in her running log: 'hip hurt today', and carry on.

It wasn't until 1980, studying abroad, that she noticed a connection between being sedentary and an increase in hip pain. She tried a short run and the pain eased. She then realised she would have to maintain a fine balance between running and resting to keep the pain at bay.

Back in Wales, a doctor recommended that she stay immobile – she was so mad at this advice that she ran home the seven miles! She sought relief from an osteopath who said 'Sorry Joan, I can help with the pain, but I can't take away the problem.' She was now running with a limp, and not making headway. Eventually she went to her doctor, who diagnosed osteo-arthritis, the result of over thirty years deterioration in her hipjoint. The hip replacement operation was recommended, but Joan had to wait until she couldn't tie her shoelaces before her condition was considered bad enough to merit priority over the waiting list!

While waiting for her operation, she canvassed readers of *Fell Runner Magazine* who had already experienced the operation. The replies were all encouraging, especially about a return to running. Her biggest morale-booster, however, was when John Disley visited her the night before the operation, only eight weeks after having had his own. She then knew everything would be all right. He told her the story of one of the first athletes to have the operation, Lord Burleigh, the 1928 Olympic 400m hurdles champion. His was a steel-on-steel model, which had to be refitted after ten years' wear. Lord Burleigh had the original ball-and-bend silver-plated and mounted on the front of his Rolls Royce, in place of the silver lady. 'After carrying me around so long,' he said, 'it deserves to have a free ride now!'

Her surgeon, who ran a bit himself, was sympathetic, but sympathy changed to alarm when she announced her intention to return to running. 'How do you know what can or can't be done with an artificial hip?' she argued. 'It's early days yet.' If there was no pain, she reasoned, it was worth a try. The surgeon took no chances with Joan, fitting her with a heavy-duty model that could take the strain of running. Apart from temporary wound discomfort, Joan's new hip felt fine. For the first six weeks, as recommended, she stayed close to home, taking short walks to strengthen the muscles. Then she graduated to longer walks in the hills, never once returning home in discomfort or needing a painkiller.

While visiting Scotland she decided to try a gentle road run of two miles, and was shocked at how long it took her. But she was more surprised to find that it wasn't her hip that bothered her but her lower back, thrown out of alignment for so long. A few more gentle runs put things right, and over the months she increased her training until she was averaging 20 miles a week. In July 1985, the annual Snowdon race was being held, and Joan wanted to take part. She reckoned she could do it if she took it easy on the descent, and did five dummy runs to convince herself it could be done. On the big day, she didn't take it as easy as she had planned; on the way down, feeling completely unfit, lungs puffing and legs rebelling, she was just glad to see the finishing line.

Joan then stepped up her training, set her sights on the marathon again.

She's lucky to have physiotherapist friends who advise her on special exercises and things to avoid. In her struggle to make a comeback, she often felt very alone, fighting the well-meaning opinion of friends and doctors that she shouldn't resume running, but never giving up hope. She's convinced that her running before the operation prevented the arthritis from immobilising her, and that it helped to ease the pain considerably.

Prostate Operation

Bryn Jenkins

According to the medical books, one out of three men in their 50s needs a prostate operation, as does one out of two men in their 60s.

It's a curious thing, but many male runners who have had a prostate operation have noticed an increase in their running speeds afterwards, although the doctors can't explain why. Bryn Jenkins is no exception: as an Over 60 he completed dozens of marathons in the last thirty years, but was never able to better a time of 3:15. After a prostate operation, however, it was a different story . . . .

Bryn Jenkins first started running in 1971, when 49, on a wager from his son. It was the annual St Neots to Huntingdon race, and Bryn had only weeks to prepare, secretly training in borrowed gear. He had been involved in boxing, football and cricket in earlier years, and it was perhaps his general fitness that helped him to finish the 12-mile race in under two hours. He joined Huntingdon AC, running cross-countries and 10-milers with them, and going on to the marathon. His first in San Diego in 1973 he finished in 3:36:39. In 1975 he had a driving accident while working for the Post Office, with a head injury that affected the blood vessels in his brain. Soon after that, a doctor told him he was also suffering from cervical spondylosis, a wasting of one of the discs in his spine. But Bryn wasn't quite ready for the wheelchair yet, so he continued his running, clocking up almost 4,000 miles in 1982 and 3,000 miles in 1983.

Training in 1983, however, was interrupted by the third in his unlucky series of ailments. He was slowing down due to a problem with his waterworks, and though he occasionally urinated blood, the pain was intermittent, so he decided not to trouble his doctor. It wasn't until he was on holiday in February that the pain got so bad he was rushed to a hospital – where it was discovered that his prostate gland had ruptured and infected one of his kidneys. The operation removed the gland and part of one kidney was well . . . . it was touch-and-go for Bryn for a few days. After the stitches came out the doctors told him not to run for six months; but after a month, Bryn got itchy feet and wanted to see what he could do. He went out for what he thought was about five minutes. Afterwards he looked at his watch and found that he had only been running for one minute! For a fortnight after that he timed himself daily and worked up to 55-minute runs. Five weeks after the operation he ran his first race: the 5-mile St Ives Fun Run, completed in 31 minutes. Then he began serious training, building up his weekly mileage to 70 miles. At this point he ran an Over 60s 15-mile race in 1:43, placing first – but he was really just building up to the Huntingdon marathon in October, 1983: which took him 2:56:54! The following year he ran the same marathon in 2:59. Both of course were very much personal bests.

Of his new-found speed after the operation, Bryn will only say that getting rid of all that excess fluid was half the battle. 'My body wasn't working correctly before the operation,' he says; 'in fact, the doctors said it was a wonder I was able to run at all!' For anyone with similar prostate symptoms Bryn advises they see their doctor straight away: 'Don't fool around with it – just because the pain and symptoms can come and go doesn't mean the condition isn't serious.'

Hearts and Pacemakers

John Atkinson

For 25 years John Atkinson ran middle distance for Barnet and District Athletic Club: 3 miles (best time 14:24, set in 1956), and 6 miles (best time 30:21, set in 1957). All was well until 1977, when John, aged 43, noticed he was beginning to feel dizzy and light-headed after a race; the feeling would often continue into the next day.

In May, 1984, the day after he had run the Cheshunt Half-marathon, he was at his desk at work when he suddenly seemed to 'spin off into the air.' He felt dizzy and peculiar; all feeling had gone from his body and he could not breathe properly. The next thing he knew he was on his way to Northwick Park Hospital, Harrow, in an ambulance. This hospital has a special ward and research centre for heart conditions. John was treated for a heart attack, but the tests proved negative; his heart, in fact, was quite strong. What the doctors did discover was that John's pulse was abnormally low, and that it continued to drop during sleep or rest periods – at one point, it dropped as low as 15 beats a minute! Oddly enough, John had no pulse problem while he was running; only while resting. For reasons still unknown, John's heart was not beating in time with his brain's oxygen requirements. He would need a pacemaker to keep it to a safe minimum and the doctors said his days of running were over. John was far from happy about this and his feelings were duly noted by the medical team.

He was discharged for a week until the doctors were ready to operate and given a temporary pacemaker to tide him over. It was a primitive contraption consisting of leads strapped to his arm and wrist and ending in a hand-held battery box that weighed 5lbs. John was terrified of tripping or falling over. When he was readmitted a week later the doctor told him: 'We've given your particular problem as a runner a lot of thought and the good news is that we can fit you with a specially developed pacemaker that will allow you to run. The bad news is that you'll have to wait another three weeks for it until the surgeon returns from holiday.' For John, the wait was well worth it.

John's pacemaker allows him to push his pulse above 100 beats a minute when exercising, but still acts to stop his pulse dropping below 50 beats a minute. The pacemaker resembles a squared-off cigarette lighter, $2\frac{1}{2}'' \times 2\frac{1}{2}''$, and is stitched an inch inside the chest wall just above the right breast. Two fine electrodes run from it down into the heart: one to the atrium to provide the beat, and one to the ventricle to regulate the flow of blood out of the heart. It is made of stainless steel and run by a micro-chip battery that won't need to be replaced for ten years. And John's check-ups are only once every six months.

When John returned to running two months later, he was understandably cautious. He was very aware of his pacemaker for the first month, and his chest felt sore. His wife Brenda, a veteran sprinter who trains with him, noticed that he was running with his arms close to his chest, as if to protect it. But he started off with a daily 3-mile run, and soon he didn't give the pacemaker another thought. He is now up to 5 miles a day, does twice-weekly interval training, and feels he has made up for lost time, taking his age into account.

Owning a pacemaker can have its droll side: John never sociali-
ses in his friends' kitchens if they have a microwave oven: the
waves can affect the programming and send the battery haywire.
And now if he pulls out in front of his clubmates in a race, they
joke that he's 'turned it up!'

Sid McSweeney

Sid McSweeney has made it back to running after open-heart
surgery, at an age when many of us would be thinking of trading in
our running shoes for a pair of bedroom slippers . . . . In 1976,
Sid, then aged 64, couldn't figure out why his race-walking was
slowing down. He'd been race-walking for thirty years, he'd
completed eighteen successive London-Brighton walks, but now
he was down from six to three mph. A visit to the doctor confirmed
that his blood pressure was high, and he was told to take it easy.
But worse was to come: angina pain flared up, and though
nitroglycerin tablets helped, he became a regular outpatient at the
Royal Free Hospital. Later an exploratory operation was
performed, and it was discovered that Sid had a blockage in his
heart. He was immediately transferred to St George's Hospital,
and three days later underwent open-heart surgery.
On his first venture out of bed a fellow patient took Sid's photo –
Sid says he looked just like a 'Belsen victim.' He was discharged
after three weeks with orders not to do anything strenuous. It was
six months before he could take a walk around the Sports grounds
near his home. He decided that swimming might be a useful aid to
recovery, but after one lap of the pool his heart was beating so hard
he feared he'd overdone it. Still, he persevered, building up
lengths daily, and six months later he was up to 80 lengths a day.
Before long Sid was back in full training. He had given up race-
walking in favour of running as his only concession, and was
thinking of competing in events alongside his running. Although
he was now over 70, he took one look at the 3.65 metres record for
the long jump in his age-group and thought 'I can do better than
that.' The last time he'd attempted the long jump was when he was
a Boy Scout!
At the European Games in Strasbourg in 1983, he broke the UK
long jump record for his age-group with a jump of 4.27m. The

200m he ran in 30 seconds. And there's been no stopping him since. At the BVAF Championships in July 1985, he clocked up six gold medals in his age-group: the long jump (4.12), high jump (1.20), shot put (8.63m – a meeting record), triple jump (7.78m), discus (21m) and Pentathlon where he was the first Over 70, with a total score of 3,341 points.

When he was 72, Sid was tested on a treadmill at the Royal Free Hospital and found to have the fitness of a 40-year-old. He's collected over fifty gold and twelve silver medals. 'The more I do,' he says, 'the better I feel.' But where does all the steely determination come from? Sid thinks back to a skinny kid who gazed at Charles Atlas photos and longed to be fit; a kid who saved up for a pair of chest-expanders and hid them under the bed so his brothers wouldn't break them. That kind of motivation is still with him.

19 ADVICE FOR THE OLDER DOG

For years I have been pressing health committees in Britain to come out boldly and rally the country round the running banner. But to no avail – they will not be bullied by me into saying that running is actually necessary for good health just because it has been a natural daily activity of the species for millions of years.

And yet the runner's best friend, the dog, gets constant reminders from *his* medical advisers of the need to keep up a regular mileage.

'To maintain your dog in a fit condition,' the veterinary surgeon will bark, 'see that he gets a good long run every day.' His justification? It is of course the fact that running is the natural way of life for a dog.

Such bluff commonsense advice was offered one day to a friend of mine, Marty Routh, a taxi-driver neighbour, by his vet – and although it was meant for his dog, not himself, it was what in the end converted him too, from being an obnoxious member of the anti-running lobby into a daily jogger.

Marty, aged 55, was one of those unbelievers content to lounge around being sarcastic about everyone else for wasting their time. 'You'll end up with a heart attack, mate,' he'd sneer. There he'd be, washing down his cab as I trotted past on my way to the local park. The sight of me fairly goaded him into insults; a form of guilt really, covering up his own disinclination to get off his backside. 'I'll outlive you all and Colonel will outlive you seven times over, you ruddy joggers,' he'd holler.

This Colonel was the pride of his life and his only true friend, a Golden Labrador, a beautiful animal. Having the charitable nature of the Labrador, it was able to behave with some kindliness to the abrasive Marty. He led it in return an over-indulgent life, chocolate biscuits, best end of lamb, that sort of thing, not to mention best end of the couch. The rule in the Routh household was that whoever came in first got the couch. Thus they were both reluctant ever to leave the cosy spot, in case the other one pinched it. Colonel was another staunch member of the anti-running lobby.

One day the dear animal began to show signs of poor health, liver probably, and Marty drove it off in his cab to see the vet.

'Handsome old fellow,' the vet greeted them, giving Colonel a chuck under the jaw.

'Not so old,' responded Marty grudgingly.

'Nine-ish? Labradors do get a bit of weight on them when they age, if you give them half a chance . . . . go to seed quickly.'

'Seven,' snapped back Marty in defensive mood. 'That's 49 really,' he added weakly. 'He'll outlive me okay.'

'H'm,' came from the vet at this odd logic. He looked at the heavy flanks and bulging belly of the dog. 'Here's the cause of the trouble. A Labrador needs a good bit of exercise, like all of us, or he'll die young.'

'Die!' cried Marty in anguish.

'No problem, start him on a couple of miles a day and he'll be with us for ages.' (Amazing, isn't it, he seemed more certain about this than your normal family doctor would be).

'Well, I'll take him for a walk,' promised Marty, though with a grimace.

'That dog needs a good *run* every day,' ended the vet, while handing over a prescription for treating the liver complaint.

This was a problem for Marty. Who was to run Colonel? He soon realised, with distaste, that there was only one candidate for the job – himself.

It forced him to think. Who could do it better than Routh himself? He could keep ahead of that dog, all right. If you asked him he could keep ahead of any of those idiotic runners in the park. From this sort of talk he adjusted his thinking very soon to the point where he was going to do a marathon. He'd get into this marathon business at the age of 55 and probably win anyway. He'd beat that Steve Cram fellow even. (His distance judgement was imperfect.)

Marty intended it to be a secret project. He'd duly let us know that we were needed to cheer him on at the finish, but not until a day or two before the 'off'.

So he set out stealthily on his opening training session. His – and

183

Colonel's. He bundled him into the cab, and drove to a little-used access road off the motorway. Out they went, the dog ahead and Marty lolloping along behind. This was to be a 10-mile slowish effort; be sure to start with an easy run, he'd read. Marty had swotted up training schedules, don't worry. When he did something, he did it well.

After 50 yards Colonel looked back at Marty with an appealing look, then graciously allowed Marty to pass him. 'That's the style,' Marty told himself. At 100 yards it was Marty deciding he needed a short recovery period and they ought to get back to base. Dog and master managed the 100 yard return journey, not very dashingly, crawled back into the cab and lay there sprawled out, breathing deeply.

Along came a squad car ten minutes later, out stepped the officers, to tap on the window and poke their noses in for suspicious smells. They ordered a breath test for Marty and had a mind to do the same for Colonel, imagining perhaps that he had figured as some sort of St. Bernard's cover-up operative in the scenario.

This didn't put Marty off running, I'm pleased to say, nor his dog, but it does, by the way, offer a demonstration that a person doesn't have it in them to go too hard before they are properly trained. You won't be able to do a 4-minute mile nor a 10-mile slow jog the first time, unless you're very athletic, and even a dog, a typical town dog, needs breaking in. My own dog once spent two days unable to get to his feet after a lovely long country run beside a swift horse. He was stiff in every muscle but duly recovered.

Here, I thought, after the Marty-Colonel episode, is a fine way to motivate the masses, the dear, dog-loving British masses. If even a taxi-driver gets to exercising anything must be possible. It's the base for a whole new running crusade whose slogan would be: If you want them to jog, get them a dog.

Running with a dog has so many advantages for a beginner. If you're self-conscious about going out at first, taking the dog gives the perfect cover – for saving blushes it's superior to the post-a-letter excuse.

Then as a dog-owner you will have that powerful need to escort the dog on his health-giving work-out even on days when you're feeling lethargic yourself. Many a well-trained animal will actually help in getting you out going to the lengths of fetching along the training shoes.

Once out the dog will want to cover more ground than you do, so the incentive to keep going is there all the time. The dog is your excuse, your incentive, your training companion and your means of self-defence – when running with a dog you will rarely be attacked by a strange animal.

Which Dog?

What sort of animal is best for the runner? The first rule is that the longer the better. Tradition has it that a dog needs each day three miles of exercise per foot of body length. Stop short only at the Great Dane, which would require 100 mile per week workouts.

In a poll I myself organised not so long ago the following breeds were highly recommended by their owners.

Border Collie One of the most popular choices. Well used to bossing around, it will see that you stay on the right lines, nose to the grindstone as it were.

Setters Irish Setters can handle a 10 miler every day of the week plus a long run on Sundays, and not even the national cross-country champion would be able to head it. The English Setter is not quite so fast but is easier to train.

Doberman What you are buying here is its reputation, which is enough to make it the perfect protector for a woman runner.

Boxer This dog is especially designed for runners who like fartlek or other broken pace workouts. It stops at every opportunity, for a twig, a ball, a bird or a lamppost, then suddenly speeds off again.

Pointer This is bred for speed, stamina and muscular endurance and can maintain a sub 6-minute pace through deep heather on hillsides all day – if *you* can't it will readily nudge you along too.

Jack Russell (The long legged variety). Praised for its ability to run in a straight line.

Labrador Even-tempered, and a gentleman, but it has the habit of wandering off for a run on its own and might not be available when needed.

Corgi Suitable for the literary type who likes to jog off to some grassy bank and curl up with a good book.

185

Once I'd completed my survey I turned to the National Canine Defence League and others for practical advice on choosing and caring for your dog, the other member of your team.

Choosing a dog

Here is this rather more official advice, from the National Canine Defence League:
● The ideal weight for a running dog is 30-70lbs, and not fat.
● Go easy on the dog until around 18 months old – it is still growing mentally and physically. That means that a puppy won't be able to help you straight away so you might want to look for an adult dog from RSPCA rescue or somewhere like Battersea Dogs' Home. If someone buys a pedigree dog they can't keep, the breed club will usually rescue it and sell it for a nominal sum providing you promise not to breed from it. But check why the dog was discarded in the first place!
● Take the dog to the vet for a comprehensive check-up, especially of its heart and its hips. Some breeds are prone to hip deformity (dysplasia) which would rule them out as runners.
● Check the dog's tendency to nervousness or aggressiveness.
● If you do buy a puppy, start young on the dog's obedience training so that by the time it is old enough to run it responds immediately to short commands. A disobedient dog is a danger to other pavement users and an embarrassment to you.
● Don't start running with a dog that is more than ten years old.
● Opinion was equally divided on the choice of a dog or a bitch.

Care of your dog

● Treat your dog as you would treat yourself. Build up its mileage gently; allow rest days; keep to a regular routine; and don't drag the dog out if it is clearly tired or under the weather.
● Make running fun – as much running off the lead as possible, with emphasis on park and grassland. Roads are as tough on a dog's paws as they are on human feet.
● Inspect the paws after each run for cuts, claws bruised at the nail bed, or wear on the pads. If the paws are bleeding after a long run,

clean them, cover and let the dog rest for a few days.

● If it has been raining, rub the dog down after the run, especially if it has a long coat. Keep the coat well groomed and always comb out burrs and twigs. If you have been running across moorland, check for ticks, especially on the legs and chest.

● Take care of your dog in crowds. Don't take it on competitive events where you could upset other runners, infuriate the race organiser and frighten the dog.

● Don't run with your dog on a very hot day. It doesn't perspire as you do and will quickly run into problems.

● Make sure your dog has enough to drink – lukewarm water is better than ice-cold.

● The dog's diet should include a fair amount of carbohydrate (eg bread, potatoes, porridge) especially if it is running more than 30mpw.

● Don't take your bitch out if she is on heat, unless you want to feel like the canine equivalent of the Pied Piper of Hamelin!

● Don't give up on your dog. The breeds recommended here all need plenty of regular exercise and your intention to run with them mustn't be short-lived.

. . . . and running away from them

Having elaborated on the benefits of running with dogs, I can't avoid mentioning another, less attractive aspect of this 'best friend' relationship; the biting dog that lurks in ambush on running trails. It's only part of a larger national problem; in this country there are 6,000,000 potential biters (only one-third of them licensed), of which each year 200,000 sink their teeth into someone. The postman is their natural and preferred prey, but when unavailable complete strangers have to serve; even, sometimes, a runner.

Statistically dog-bites come half way down the list of risks to road runners. (I quote figures compiled by the methodically-minded people of Atlanta, Georgia):

Out of every 100,000 miles run:

Eleven runners were . . . . hit by thrown objects

Six runners were . . . . bitten by dogs

One runner was . . . . hit by a car

A British survey found (1) that three times as many men as

women are bitten by dogs and (2) that the dogs with the highest biting ratings were Alsatians, Sheep Dogs and Retrievers. Thus it is that the dogs that bite the most are the biggest dogs . . . . and the biggest dogs are the ones with the biggest bites.

But whether the victim of big bite or small, you must report for a tetanus injection at the nearest casualty department as soon as possible, and then you must inform the police of the incident. The local police station will take down the owner's name and address if you have noted it, or will ask for identifying marks from which they may be able to check him out on their register of previous offenders.

Dogs and the law

The police will then attempt to find the owner and caution him. If the dog continues to bite he is in trouble. When his name has appeared on the register three times he may be taken to court, where his owner will be ordered to keep him under control . . . . or have him destroyed!

So, on being threatened by a dog you would be advised as a first step to read out to him his legal risks involved in taking such action. You could also offer him a copy of the leaflet prepared by the Joint Advisory Committee on Pets in Society and the Institute of Park and Recreation Administration, recommending that he 'at all times respects the rights of other park users.'

But what if it's your dog which has bitten someone else? Heaven forbid, even another runner! Know that your dog has rights and may not lightly be injured by the victim's defending himself. To quote from *Your Dog and the Law*[1]: 'It seems clear that there would have to be some correlation between the severity of the dog's attack and the severity of the counter-measures used. At one extreme, to kill a dog following a nip in the leg would not be justified, yet at the other, a person is not required to fear for his life before hurting the dog.'

If your dog is wrongfully killed or injured by another person you will be able to sue and recover damages for his loss.

[1] Godfrey Sandys-Winsch (Shaw & Sons Ltd) 1984

Evasive Action

Thus a runner would be advised against the defensive kick. Best of all is to avoid the confrontation in the first place, to accept that discretion, even actual flight, is the better part of valour. Safer even than flight is to slow down rapidly when trouble looms.

Some runners have found that it is additionally effective while slowing down to fix the dog with a fierce and concentrated stare. It puts him off – I might say that almost anyone would be put off by a fixed stare from the bruisers that come up with this theory.

Here is the official point of view on warding off bites.

Dr Roger Mugford, a psychologist who specialises in animal behaviour, says dogs are motivated to attack by two trigger factors: moving objects and antagonistic gestures. He adds that Corgis and Collies are particularly responsive to the 'chase-play' game. When they see you running along, the 'chase-play' mechanism sets them off and they follow in hot pursuit. When you see this happening, do not continue to run as this encourages the dog to further play or possible attack. Stop immediately and remain motionless with your arms across your chest or held in the air – do not flail them about. Remain as passive as possible until the animal gets bored with your lack of response and moves on.

On no account aim a kick at the dog. Dr Mugford explains that this will build up his antagonism and he will chase and bite other runners to get his own back.

When running past owners with their dogs, give them a wide berth particularly those on a lead. They are more likely to lunge at your passing parts than dogs who are not. Alsatians are particularly possessive of their owners and should be given a miss on or off the lead.

If you are running in the country, establish a regular track for yourself and avoid farms and running through field or farm gates.

Defensive Weaponry

Here are the means of last resort now on the market to arm the runner against persistent pirate dogs.

The Doggie Tapper (see Chapter 15) This is a long stick with a nasty spring at the end, for biting back.

The Galton Touch There is also available a small cylindrical dog whistle which when pressed emits a loud high-frequency alarm almost inaudible to humans but scaring to a dog.

20 ROME DIARY

Without doubt the peak of your career as a veteran runner will be competing in an international meeting. There are no bars to entry and no qualifying processes, just so long as you are an accredited member of the vets. It's your own decision and you'd be well advised to go. It'll be a high point in your life. Of course you have to pay your way – the travel costs to the venue, which might be anywhere in the world, and the entry fees – but the event always combines marvellously as a holiday in its own right. Thus the net cost is zero!

There's one of these internationals each year: world championships in the odd-numbered years and European championships in the evens.

To preserve the excitement and flavour of the last one I attended, the World Veteran Games, Rome, of June, 1985, I kept a diary of my activities. It was a very busy period for me as I was there in several different capacities. These were competitor, head of the British delegation at conferences of the world body, reporter for *Running* Magazine and also spectator, noisily encouraging friends entered in various of the 400 events going on in four different stadia.

Here is my day-to-day diary of the Games.

Saturday (June 22) From the start it's clear that these are going to be Games of pomp and ceremony. Just consider the two premier stadia being used, the portentous 1960 Olympic track with nine lanes and the Stadio Marmi – a marble folly erected by Mussolini, which is fenced in by fifty grandiose and rather comical statues of naked sportsmen. They all look a bit like Mussolini, even the heavy-jawed cricketer dressed in nothing but his pads.

At a press conference I met five important competitors – Willie Davenport, high-hurdles gold medallist at the Mexico Olympics, now 42; Parry O'Brien, shot putt winner at Helsinki and Melbourne; Thane Baker, gold and silver sprinter at two Olympics; Sister Marion the Flying Nun and Gabriela Andersen-Schiess, who did that sensational stagger around the last lap of the LA marathon.

The day was so packed with events and confrontations that by evening even the commentator spoke of the morning's events as 'yesterday's'. Action runs from 8.30am up to midnight, except during the long siesta.

There are 4,400 competitors from 47 nations and I am one of 62 entrants in the 100 metres for Men Over-60. Owing to poor planning by the organisers we are obliged to sort out the nine places for the finals just by heats as they'd omitted semi-finals. I didn't think I had much chance of winning a medal, in spite of having a tremendous season behind me.

In the baking sun the older veteran's usual difficulty of warming up is avoided. I managed to win my heat in 13.06 sec. However time is the deciding factor and Ubarri (from Puerto Rico and an ex-Olympian) did 12.58 sec. The next eight of us are bunched between 13.01 and 13.08 sec. We won't find out who will go forward to the final until the next day – another black mark for the organisers. While watching the 10,000 metre races I saw a number of breakdowns in lap-scoring, which caused heartbreak to many.

This was followed by a great deal of criticism and political intrigue. The organisers said 'never mind' and Primo Nebiolo, president of the IAAF, took the opportunity to make speeches.

Sunday I spent the day concentrating on my 100m final, my only real chance in the Games. I knew there was a possibility of a bronze medal because after the likely winners, Ubarri and Valentine, the rest of us were on equal terms. If I got my pick-up right I could beat Kleinmann, Hoyer and Sobrero, all ahead of me at Brighton last year in the European championships. In 1984 I had a doubtful hamstring but now I have perfect mobility and felt tremendous in the still, warm evening, in spite of being, at almost 65, the oldest man in the group.

I started well but then drifted back behind Hoyer, Sobrero, and Yamazaki, as well as the leaders. At halfway I was lying seventh with the Canadian, Baum, also in front of me. My adrenaline responded, I told myself 'go for the bronze' and I visibly put in a kick.

At 90 metres I was sixth and beginning to cruise through the pack. At 95 metres I passed Hoyer and moved into fourth place. I heard the crowd exclaim at my final acceleration and at 99 metres I overtook Valentine. Then, on the line, I managed to edge out Yamazaki too.

The results were: 1 Ubarri 12.60 sec; 2 Stein 13.00 sec; 3 Yamazaki, also with 13.00 sec.

Monday I devoted today to old friends; many of us have been competing in these Games since they were established in Toronto in 1975. There is a marvellous international camaraderie everywhere.

The most contentious item among the organisers of world veteran affairs is the proposal by the world athletic body, the International Amateur Athletic Federation, to adopt us officially. This is an important accolade for the vets, but there are those who have reservations, especially among the US masters. Their reasons hinge on the idea that this would oblige us to ban South Africa. However it is known that on every occasion of these Games, the host nation itself has always objected to South African teams. I'm a well-known – nay, notorious – opponent of apartheid, so it's clear why I am in favour of joing the IAAF.

Nevertheless to me it seems equally relevant that it will give us some standing in the athletics world, and is a move towards granting older age groups equal respect and equal opportunity. In Britain especially we need acceptability; do you know that although we represent something like thirty per cent of the running community here we have no representation at national level? Would we have been allowed to stage a marathon, like in Rome, through the streets of the capital? Could we have produced £250,000 from the government, as the Australians have been promised for the Games in 1987? No, when setting up the European championships in Brighton last year, the authorities *loaned* us £2,000.

Tuesday There was some marvellous racing today. John Gilmour of Australia has won the men's Over-65 10,000m and is expected to take golds in the other distance events too. Throughout the day there was a series of exciting men's and women's 5,000m finals. In the Women's Over 35s, the British woman Carol Borrill has already won the gold in the 10,000m, but passes up the 5,000m with her eye on the cross-country two days later. The Italian Cesarina Toroni took it instead in 18:09. The Dane, Ella Grimm was second.

There was also a series of exciting 200m semi-finals, including the spectacular effort by our *Running* protégé Ron Taylor, whose fluidity of motion at 51 years old is remarkable.

'Keep those arms swinging like a pendulum,' he tells the rest of the British team, 'look at me, they're giving me so much momentum I can't stop before I'm halfway around the next bend.'

My own semi-final was omitted again. I scraped into the next day's finals, once more seventh-fastest in the heats.

Wednesday Somehow I lack motivation for the 200m final today. I conscientiously set aside an hour for a siesta (to bring my pulse rate down) and later did my warm-up routine (to bring it up). Then I ran a slow mile, plus extensive calisthenics and stretching and some hard striding to bring out a sweat. But I didn't have that devilish spite in me. More seriously, my training this year has been focused on pure sprinting, which paid off in the 100m. The 200m is more like a long distance event for me!

I had a go anyway, and again I was lying fifth 10 metres from the end. This time though I was still fifth at the tape.

At the marble stadium, the Marmi, I sat with British friends to cheer on Les Roberts in the Men Over-40 5,000m. He led all the way round, with Patrick Murphy of Ireland on his shoulder, then pulled away to run a staggering last lap in 60 seconds.

Thursday A Dutchman, Frans Buys, a new arrival in the Over-60s group and a new convert to athletics, takes the Over-60 high hurdles (100m) in 16.02 sec. Britain's Les Williams stumbled at the start and missed his deserved medal. Judy Vernon, ex-international, now in the Over-35 age group led all the way in the sprint hurdles but crashed through the final two barriers to finish fourth.

Rumours abound that Cesare Becalli is to stand for world president against the reigning Don Farquharson of Canada. Cesare is the man who has staged these games – will the poor organisation tell against him?

In my 400m heats, I finished about twentieth fastest, with a time of 68 sec. Six men over-60 years old have gone under one minute. This proves that my specific training was right, if I'd done better in the 400m, I'd have been slower in my sprint.

In the general meeting of the world vets organisation we decided after a long and tough debate to go in with the IAAF. John Holt, permanent secretary of the IAAF, presented the case brilliantly. Becalli decided to pull out of the presidential race, and Farquharson was re-elected.

Friday The temperature for the cross-country was in the 80s. Four laps were run on the Hippodrome horsetrack, with no shade – and no water. We all broke the rules by offering the runners a drink and a few spectators sprayed water over some competitors. In the Over-40s group Guy Ogden led most of the way, but faded to seventh. The winner was Roger Robertson from New Zealand. Ron Franklin was fifth in the Over-55s, in spite of a calf injury.

In the adjourned session of the general meeting, we voted to go to Melbourne in two years time, but the venue after that is undecided. Perhaps the US will put up for the Games in 1989 or maybe some of us British martyrs will do it.

Saturday The most exciting athletics yet: first, the whole series of 400m finals from oldest to youngest. The spry 86-year-old Paul Spangler got round in under 2 minutes as sole Over-85 competitor. The Over-40 race was won by George Smith, Canada, in 50.10 (John Henson GB came second). Britain's Peter Higgins, an ex-Olympian, won the Over-55 age-group in 54.84 sec.

Each 1,500m final ended in a breathtaking climax. Can you imagine the pleasure of having some twenty superb races set out before you one after another?

Sunday A traditional marathon ending which went through the heart of Rome and somehow the Italian traffic was kept at bay. It was very hot and there was not much water available, but no one seemed to suffer from more than a few moments of heat exhaustion. There was a long queue of winners on the medal rostrum at

195

the end of the race, which was shown on Italian, German and Japanese TV . . . . but not British.

The traditional relays closed the Games, but after the 4×100m the organisation suffered its final let-down, and was obliged to cancel the 4×400m, even though the competitors were all warmed up and waiting for it.

By the end of the nine days you feel far fitter than at any other time. These internationals are a perfect health cure as well as athletic contest.

EPILOGUE

Running has one benefit even more remarkable than that of boosting health and fitness, or ending the cigarette habit or offering fun outdoors – it can completely transform the lives of people depressed by personal failure, to turn them into confident achievers. I have seen this happen countless times among acquaintances, both men and women, sometimes married couples.

Here I merge these many people into one disenchanted family, the Jacksons. It is fiction, because these Jacksons don't exist, but I've heard bits of their story from various veteran runners to whom I have spoken.

The Also-runner's Tale

Telling of the life of Jonathan Jackson and his wife Josephine . . . . of how he became cheesed off, then brassed off, then dejected, then depressed . . . . of what he did about it, which was nothing . . . . of what *she* did about it . . . . and how that worked for him too . . . . and how his victory over the marathon brought him eventual victory in the Weather Office as well.

Jonathan Jackson, of Hemel Hempstead, aged 40, was one of the world's also-runners, those important people who serve to make up the numbers in any race. After tremendous dedication in training, he and his team had worked their way through the field from the start at Greenwich to a sight of the finish, and a sight of the medals, too, when real danger threatened . . . .

But let us go back first a year or two to the time when Johathan, aged 39 and 6 months, had been bumping along at the bottom of a long downer in his life. It had started with a sticky patch in his job, then he had permitted himself to become blindly envious of his

197

wife's brilliant career, contrasting her lucky breaks with his own unluckiness. Envy caught him in its grip.

It had got so that he couldn't concentrate on his own problems to pull himself out of the ditch he was in, but could merely cast green-eyed looks over towards her. This left him further depressed, and the depression left him even less able to take a hold on himself.

His only resource was to nurse a chip on his shoulder about everything instead of blaming himself.

'Nice day,' friends would greet him good-naturedly, knowing he needed cheering up, 'sun's come out after all'.

'Don't lay it on *me*,' he'd reply ungraciously. (Point is he worked in the weather forecasting department!)

Josephine, his wife, could sense the problem that was disturbing him and did what she could not to parade her success before him, but in the past year she had shot half-way to the Top of the Pops. She was a singer who had now hit just the right note, and her name became something of a household word, which, rather unfortunately, made his name so, too. New acquaintances would sometimes, by a slip, say 'Oh, you're *Mister* Josephine Jackson, how'd ya do,' adding to his chagrin.

Her fame robbed him as well of the only bit of glamour in his life – his occasional appearances on TV, where he could be seen in a professional role; after some years' backroom instruction in moving little black clouds about on the wallmap, his was the face, when the senior weatherman was on holiday, that pronounced those words of doom: 'Rain, rain and more rain.'

It had been pleasing to him to have the neighbours recognise him, and to know that his two children were proud of such a famous father. But now he was outshone by Josephine's greater and growing fame on TV.

So if you said 'Nice day' to him when he'd prophesied the opposite, you could certainly expect a flea in the ear.

Josephine managed not only a career, but gourmet cooking, her own splendid home dress-making and the bringing up of the two children as well. All so effortlessly and capably – could anything serve to choke Jonathan more?

As he looked in the mirror one day Jonathan thought he could see what it was that had loaded the dice against him. He was almost forty and thus passing right through the promotion zone, maybe forever. Fame and professional success would elude him, he'd remain always in his own wife's shadow.

Look at that: grizzly untamed moustache, stringy hair and a sagging stomach. He'd have to do something about that stomach he told himself, and immediately, in the way of the depressed, did nothing.

What could you do about turning 40, he sighed? What was needed here was a miracle, but do you get miracles these days?

At this point a small miracle did occur, in a complicated, roundabout way, as follows: Josephine was herself not without something of a middle-age spread, which now brought problems to her too, for she'd decided to spend her new earnings all on dresses for herself, instead of on the home, which Jonathan would find unacceptable as a kind of criticism of his limited ability to support the family.

Having to deal with fashionable dressmakers she became very self-conscious about her shape and decided to do something about it right away. She took up jogging.

She went out early in the morning to jog around the block; she jogged as far as the first lamp post, then finding this made her puff walked to the next lamp post, then jogged again, then walked and so on – ten posts altogether. (She'd obviously had the best guidance.)

It didn't take many weeks before she could go right round the local park in one sustained jog. Unfortunately now she hit a spot of unpleasantness. An idiot man shouted at her 'Hup! Pick up your feet, Josephine!' He'd recognised her from the box.

She felt she could never go out again alone. 'Won't you come out with me Jon?' she asked her husband.

Instead of offering sympathy, he chucked one of the children's balaclavas at her: 'Pull that over your face, no one'll recognise you.'

'Now I look like a mugger myself,' she said cheerily.

But she was back again with more little fears the next day. This time two young lads had tried to pick her up. 'They were only eleven,' she complained tearfully.

'Well, take off the balaclava,' responded Jonathan unhelpfully. 'That'll put 'em off.'

However she insisted the next time that he came out with her for

199

support. He pulled on some plimsolls and an old pair of gardening pants and trailed grumpily along over to the park. 'Now just jog a little, then when you're tired walk a little,' she explained to him importantly. 'No harm at all in walking a while and you'll soon get used to it.'

Here's the miracle. He got used to it immediately . . . . in fact he kept up with her easily, without even having to walk, then dashed ahead, and she found him at the end of the run, legs crossed, waiting for her to catch up.

Here was one thing he could do better than her!

He was quite ready to go out with her again the next day, and the next, and wasn't even put off on those nasty mornings when he'd warned the population the night before of 'rain clearing, followed by widespread showers.'

Here is the schedule he worked up for himself, eminently suitable for a beginner who is a natural.

Week 1 He happily ran a steady couple of miles without feeling any strain. He had a definite desire to go farther, rather than faster. Back home after his run he bubbled over in explaining to Josephine how easy and pleasant it was, if you knew how: whereas she always experienced the after-effects for an hour or two.

Week 2 At the end of his run, before Josephine arrived, he doubled back to add another mile to the daily total. He didn't feel as if he had really been extended.

Week 3 A mystery arose now: Josephine noticed during this wettish week that there were waffle-marks from running shoes on her carpets one morning, though they weren't proposing to do their family jog until evening. Yes, Jonathan didn't want to own up to it but he was ducking out to do a secret session on one day a week. The body demanded it! So his schedule now amounted to 2 or 3 miles four times a week and 5 miles on another day – some 15 miles weekly. That began to produce a marked training effect in him.

200

Week 4 The extent of this aerobic effect could actually be measured by his fourth week, for he could read how swiftly his pulse beat returned to normal after the run.

Week 5 With a month of slow stuff behind him our beginner could now think of speed work. Jonathan ventured to set himself a series of time trials and duly cut down his time for a lap of the park to 8 minutes 32 seconds, a distance he optimistically put at between 2½ and 3 miles.

Josephine, whom we have left half way round the park, found this eight minutes stuff not of much service to her, but she was pleased anyway to see him with an interest. She could observe how he concentrated when on these fast runs of his: he sailed through the pain, by dint of keeping his mind on the task, and at the finish had a sense of fulfilment.

Jonathan was beginning to build up his belief in himself. He could feel it. In general he had a new confidence that he could get things done, that he could measure himself against other people, and here we go . . . . why not maybe beat the Ovetts and Coes, certainly on his home course? He'd sit on their shoulders and sprint past them on that bumpy dip just before the gate.

And, very important to Jonathan the man: he certainly had found something he could upstage Josephine in.

This marked the time when he joined the Aldwych Also Rans, a lunch-hour club of marathoners in their 30s and 40s not all under the three hour mark, by any means. They had a superb and expert coach among them, though, who worked them through a fort-nightly training schedule adapted from his own strenuous programme. They did one hard week, and one soft week. In the hard week they mixed in days of fartlek, hills and fast quarter-miles with jog recovery. In the slow week there was some long-slow-distance, some easy stuff and always some days off.

Jonathan entered a couple of scratch fun runs and competed for the Also Rans in a match against the local veterans. Then he found himself, with three other Over 40s from his club, in the London Marathon – he hadn't believed for a moment that his entry would come through the ballot, but when it did he knew he had to run.

All this had taken but seven months, yet quite a change had

come over him. One thing: that stately stomach had gone back into its shell, although he ate better than before. He'd dropped smoking as a waste of energy. He slept better too, and most amazing of all he found himself enjoying the company of Josephine's grand show biz friends, especially when they asked him admiringly about his running.

For the next few months he concentrated on the London. Concentration, what does it mean? It means a clear head, attention to the subject under attack, strong motivation – and confidence. All this he had picked up from running and training.

Without that ability to go for what is important, bringing out the reality of the moment, he would never have been able to manage his training for the marathon. He stuck to the schedule suggested by one of the star marathon names of the past, as printed in his newspaper, and doggedly went through the last weeks of training, with the long, long run, the pain of interval training, and the day of rest just prior to the race, when he employed himself cooking a succession of pasta meals for himself and a grateful family.

He was very pleased the evening before to have to broadcast the information to the world that marathon day was going to be nice and drizzly! What could be better for the runners than cool, damp weather?

On the day it was simply to be a matter of running 26 miles. Oh, yes, simple.

It turned out to be misty at daybreak, he was pleased to note, exactly as predicted, and he made no attempt to tank up on liquid, which might be uncomfortable gurgling about in the stomach, in spite of the coach's orders to drink. The first 12 miles he positively raced through, again against the advice of his illustrious Olympic expert, who said don't go out too fast. Could that turn out to be his downfall? He thought, himself, that he had speeded up through not wasting time as others had in stopping for drinks at the feeding stations. The mist, mind you, seemed to have melted by the start and things became in fact sunny and warm, but he believed this was just a passing phase and it must cool down again. So the forecast had it. So no drinks.

He had raced off at the start, secondly, because he'd felt so fine and let himself be carried away by the crowd; at almost every step he reckoned he needed to show those who were lining the course, some of whom recognised him, just what speed he was capable of.

When he arrived at the half-way mark he began to sense trouble. When he reached the Embankment he felt defeated, when he dragged into Trafalgar Square he was done up. The sun was still belting away and the other runners were crowding the feeding stations, but he still wouldn't touch a drink. Didn't have the time to spare. Only a few miles to go. Sure to turn cold and wet anyway, as promised, within the next few minutes . . . .

So he lurched along at a very undistinguished pace indeed, until in the end he rolled to a complete stop. No, the crowd weren't having this – they howled at him. They weren't having their weather man let them down, even if the weather had let him down. In the depths of his conscience there was another small group he couldn't let down, his fellow Also Rans, who were going for that team medal in the Over 40 stakes.

So he broke into an agonising trot again, keeping the looming Buckingham Palace so firmly in his sights that it imprinted itself on his retina.

That image stayed with him deludedly even after he had turned off into Birdcage Walk. As a matter of fact absolutely all that he remembered of the last part of the race was slogging up the Mall towards the Palace. He was dehydrated, and this was a symptom of it. The remainder of his run can be easily reconstructed from evidence on camera: he *did* turn down Birdcage Walk for the last mile but now gradually began to weave and wander, while ordinary members of the public yelled him on and his own clubmates screamed him on.

He kept moving, determined to prove himself, now walking, now jogging, as if it were a lamp-post to lamp-post beginner's session, going also from the extreme right of the roadway to the extreme left, almost under the feet of other runners.

Then there was 100 yards only remaining – and calamity! – he stumbled to a stop, before very gently and very slowly crumpling downwards to ground level, first at the knees, then at the hips, until he was sitting in a heap.

Now no one howled, it seemed too cruel to urge on this broken man. But he picked himself up again and tottered another few yards. Then he slumped again. He couldn't possibly make it. He couldn't even stand himself up. He would start to scramble to his feet then the elegant crumpling-up act would happen.

However – yes, however you explain it, there was still a small final stage of his miracle left and it got him up and carried him over the line. Here someone immediately wrapped him up warmly and forced on him a few mouthfuls of water. At that moment his professional pride was itself also saved: for by now, more than three hours after the start, the sun *had* finally shone its last, to be obscured by some depressing-looking clouds. Jonathan looked up in triumph from where he lay. 'S'raining,' he croaked, shaking an aggressive fist at the heavens, 'told you it would.'

Of course all the final moments of his race had been covered by the cameras, there's nothing they enjoy more than a human being's great personal struggle. They pictured him with his reward of a team bronze medal too and now Jonathan was famous. Who hadn't witnessed that heart-rending sight!

It wasn't long before he was selected for promotion as front man in the weather department. No doubt that his work had improved: he deserved it. (It wasn't his fault that the sun on that marathon day, as on many another, flatly contradicted the plans forecast for it.)

From then on Jonathan was able to behave far more kindly, even patronisingly, to his wife, who poor thing, didn't log up nearly as much airtime over the year as he did.

Pity though that she hadn't been able to persevere with her commitment to running.

Well, it would not really have done, would it, for Mrs Josephine Jackson to have maybe picked up a gold or silver medal some time? That could have caused problems.

Yet it must be noted that somehow she managed to keep her weight down to a reasonable level. What was the explanation of that mystery? Was it connected with the damp waffle-marks, ladies' size, to be spied very early in the morning in the Jackson hallway from time to time?

BEATING YOUR HEART
by Richard Adler

FINDING OUT YOU HAVE CORONARY HEART
DISEASE COULD BE THE BEST THING THAT CAN
HAPPEN TO YOU, NOT THE WORST ... BECAUSE
NOW YOU CAN DO SOMETHING ABOUT IT.

Twenty years ago, Richard Adler was told that he was well on
his way towards a massive heart attack. At first he didn't believe
it. Then he realised that he'd *better* believe it. He was lucky – he
found out in time.

BEATING YOUR HEART is *the* handbook to guide and
reassure those hundreds and thousands of people in this country
who suffer from coronary heart disease. It tells how *you* can find
out if you are 'at risk'. (A heart attack needn't be your first
indication that you have coronary heart disease.) It describes the
risk factors and how they can be dealt with. It's not just a
question of medicine and what the doctors can do – it's also a
matter of diet, exercise and most importantly – lifestyle. A lifestyle of 'moderation' is what saved Richard Adler from that
heart attack – and it can save you!

BEATING YOUR HEART tells what your odds are and how
to 'beat' them. The people who fear they are at risk of a heart
attack, the coronary heart disease sufferers and their families
should read this book and *take heart*. Because reading it could be
the first step towards recovery, the first day of the rest of your
life.

0 552 12697 7   £1.95

THE CORGI BOOK OF BICYCLES AND BICYCLING
by Peter Dobson

More and more people are taking to bicycles, not only for fitness, relaxation or sport, but also as a means of transport. Bikes are not only cheaper to run than a car – they can often get you there sooner!

Written by an experienced enthusiast, THE CORGI BOOK OF BICYCLES AND BICYCLING tells you all you need to know about buying, using and enjoying a bicycle:

* What kind of bicycle do you need? * Building your own bike. * Accessories. * Locks and insurance. * Safety. * Detailed and practical information on the maintenance of your bike,

plus chapters on the history of the bicycle . . . how it all began . . . the adventure (and discomfort!) of the early years of cycling.

THE CORGI BOOK OF BICYCLES AND BICYCLING is liberally illustrated with black and white photographs and detailed line drawings, and contains a comprehensive list of useful names and addresses, a list of further reading, and an index for easy reference.

0 552 99069 8   £2.95

THE FAST MEN
by David Frith

Revised and up-dated edition.

CRICKET'S MOST THRILLING SPECTACLE!

A compelling collection of anecdotes, facts and figures about Willis, Lillee, Thomson, Hogg, Croft, Roberts, Garner, Hadlee, Imran Khan and many, many more international speed giants.

'An excellent book'
The Times

'An astonishing number of facts ... an essential book for anyone who enjoys reading about cricket and who at the same time delights in being interested and amused'
The Guardian

'Makes your hair stand on end'
Daily Mail

0 552 10435 3   £2.95

A SELECTED LIST OF NON-FICTION TITLES
AVAILABLE FROM CORGI BOOKS

While every effort is made to keep prices low, it is sometimes necessary to increase prices at short notice. Corgi Books reserve the right to show new retail prices on covers which may differ from those previously advertised in the text or elsewhere.

The prices shown below were correct at the time of going to press.

ORDER FORM

All these books are available at your book shop or newsagent, or can be ordered direct from the publisher. Just tick the titles you want and fill in the form below.

CORGI BOOKS, Cash Sales Department, P.O. Box 11, Falmouth, Cornwall.

Please send cheque or postal order, no currency.

Please allow cost of book(s) plus the following for postage and packing:

U.K. Customers—Allow 55p for the first book, 22p for the second book and 14p for each additional book ordered, to a maximum charge of £1.75.

B.F.P.O. and Eire—Allow 55p for the first book, 22p for the second book plus 14p per copy for the next seven books, thereafter 8p per book.

Overseas Customers—Allow £1.00 for the first book and 25p per copy for each additional book.

NAME (Block Letters) ....

ADDRESS ....

....